The ABC's of CHEMISTRY

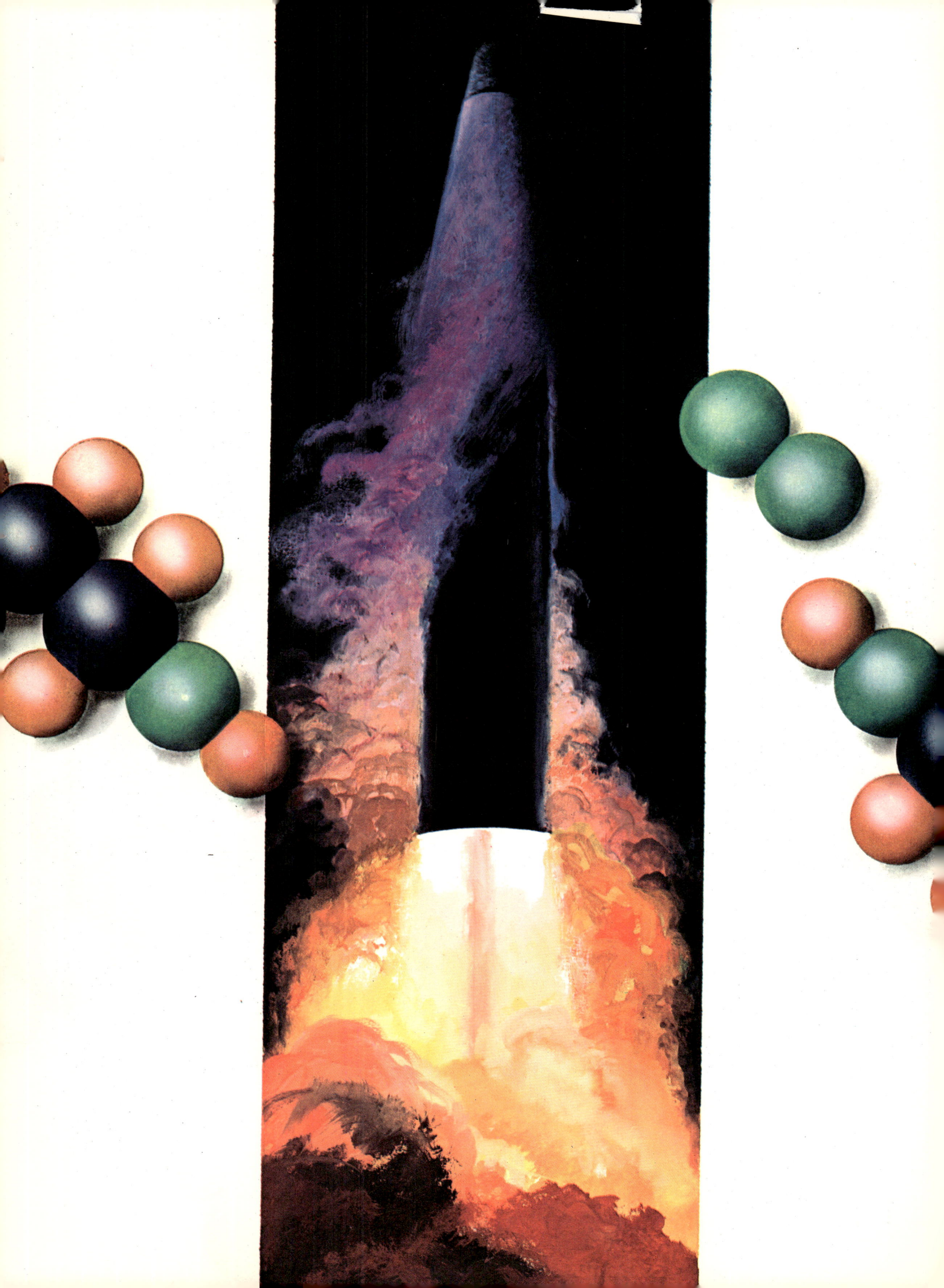

THE ABC's OF
CHEMISTRY

AN ILLUSTRATED DICTIONARY

ROY A. GALLANT

Illustrated by JOHN POLGREEN

DOUBLEDAY & COMPANY, INC., GARDEN CITY, NEW YORK

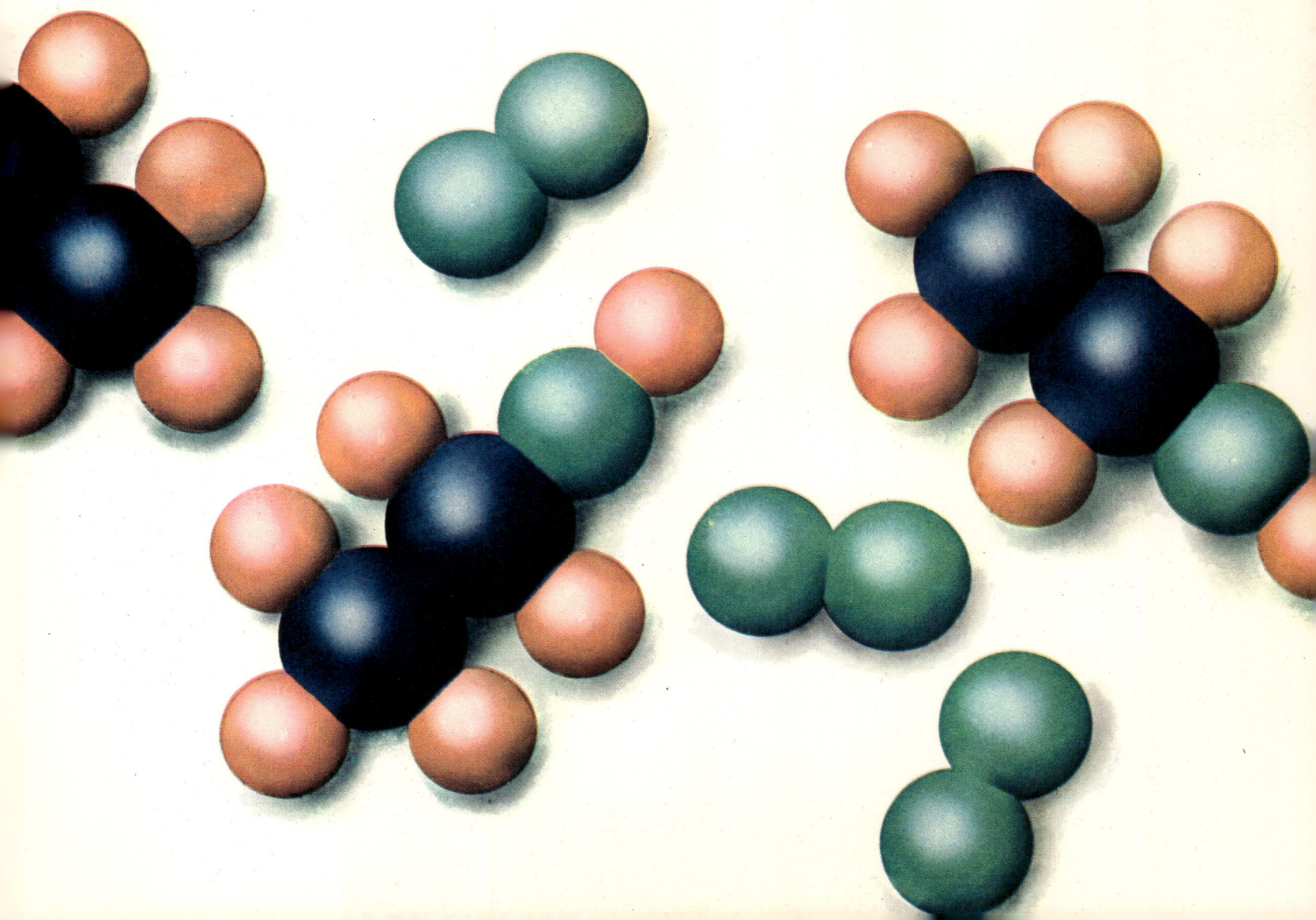

FOR JONATHAN AND JAMES

Other Books by ROY A. GALLANT

EXPLORING THE MOON   EXPLORING CHEMISTRY

EXPLORING MARS   EXPLORING THE PLANETS

EXPLORING THE UNIVERSE   MAN'S REACH INTO SPACE

EXPLORING THE WEATHER   EXPLORING UNDER THE EARTH

EXPLORING THE SUN   ABC'S OF ASTRONOMY

The author's thanks to W. R. Abell, who is Head of the Science Department of the Central American High School, London, for his many helpful suggestions and guidance. The illustrator's thanks to Thomas Stuart, Dobbs Ferry High School, New York, for his advice about the illustrations appearing in this book.

The tables on pp. 63 and 86 are based on tables in *Chemistry and You* (1957) by Baker, et al., and are printed by permission of the publisher, Lyons & Carnahan.

CONTENTS

DICTIONARY OF TERMS

A

Abrasive A substance used to polish or grind another substance. Sand and emery are both abrasive materials.

Absolute Scale Also known as the Kelvin scale; written as °K. or °A. To convert from °C. to °K., add 273 to the centigrade reading. Therefore, 20°C. would equal 293°K., and 40°C. would equal 313°K., and so on; 0°K. equals −273°C. This is known as *Absolute Zero*. At this temperature all molecular motion is thought to stop. However, temperatures below this have been reached in the laboratory.

Absorption A soaking through of one material into another; for example, water into a sponge; a gas in water. (See also *Adsorption*.)

sponge

absorbed liquid

liquid

Porous materials such as a sponge and wood soak up liquids. Heat and light can also be absorbed.

Acetone A colorless liquid and an excellent solvent $(CH_3)_2CO$. It dissolves resins, gums, and varnishes, and is used to make dyes and chloroform. Acetone is a ketone. (See *Ketone*.)

Acetylene C_2H_2. A colorless, poisonous, flammable gas, prepared when water drops on calcium carbide (CaC_2). It is used in "carbide" lighting, in oxyacetylene welding torches, and as a starting, or parent, material in the preparation of many organic compounds.

Acid Any substance which liberates hydrogen ions in solution. When an acid reacts with a base it forms a salt and water. (See special section on acids, p. 83.)

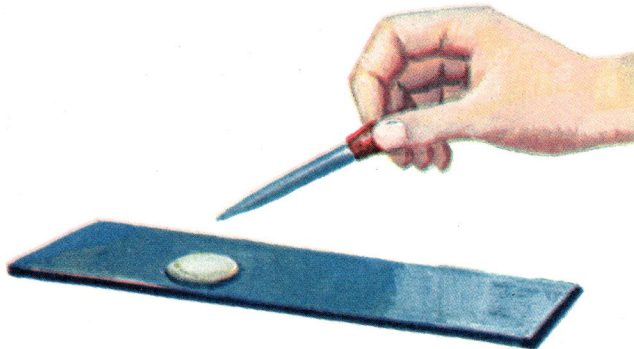

In general, acids react with active metals by producing salt and releasing hydrogen.

Acid Anhydride An oxide (such as sulfur trioxide—SO_3) that forms an acid when combined with water.

ACTH A hormone produced by the forward part of the pituitary. It acts on the adrenal glands and is concerned with growth control and sexual maturity. (See also *Hormones*.)

Actinide Elements In the periodic table, the series of radioactive elements beginning with actinium—elements with atomic numbers 89 through 103. Some of these elements are found in nature, but others are elements made by man in atom smashers. (See *Periodic Table*, p. 68.)

Activated Charcoal Charcoal which has been treated (by heating in steam and air) to rid it of tarry impurities. The result is increased porosity and, therefore, a more effective adsorbing area (see *Adsorption*). Charcoal which has been *activated* this way has a remarkable power of adsorbing gases, hence its use in gas masks.

Activity The relative ease with which one element combines with another to form a compound.

Activity Series (See *Electromotive Series*.)

Addition Reaction A chemical reaction which produces a new compound formed by the addition of an atom (or group) to a molecule—for example, when 2 atoms of bromine are added to an ethylene molecule to form ethylene dibromide. (See *Unsaturated Compound, Polymerization.*)

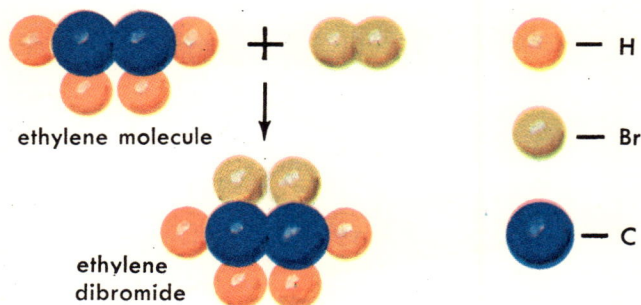

ethylene molecule

ethylene dibromide

— H

— Br

— C

Adhesion Molecular forces which enable one substance to stick to the surface of another substance.

Adrenalin A hormone known as methyl-amino-ethanol catechol—$C_9H_{13}NO_3$. (See also *Hormones.*)

Adsorption The formation of a film of molecules of a dissolved substance upon the surface of a solid. Adsorption (as opposed to absorption) is only a surface effect.

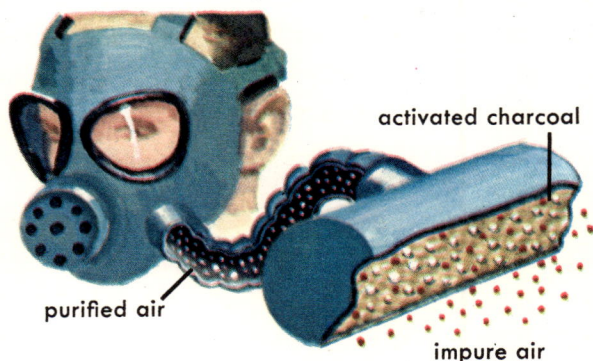

activated charcoal

purified air

impure air

As air passes through the activated charcoal of a gas mask, impurities are adsorbed at the surface.

Aeration of Water The third stage in the purification process of drinking water. The water is sprayed into the air so that impurities causing offensive odors and taste are oxidized. (See *Water Purification* diagram.)

Air A mixture of the gases making up the earth's atmosphere: 78% nitrogen, 21% oxygen, 1% other gases, including argon, helium, neon, ozone, and carbon dioxide.

Alchemy The ancient and fruitless attempt to change base metals into gold by chemical means.

Alcohol A class of organic compounds having one or more hydroxyl (OH) groups attached to the molecule, where a hydrogen atom normally would be. For example, methanol.

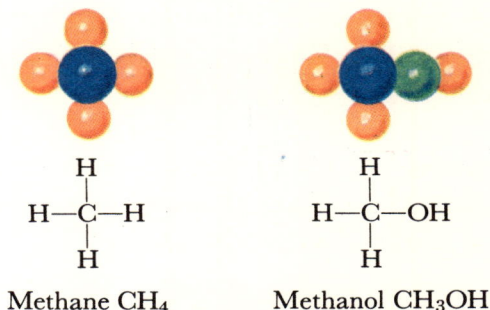

H
|
H—C—H
|
H

Methane CH_4

H
|
H—C—OH
|
H

Methanol CH_3OH

1. **Absolute**—100% alcohol, also called pure alcohol; 2. **Denatured**—alcohol (ethanol) intended for industrial use and which has been made poisonous or unpalatable so that it is unsuitable for drinking. Methanol or pyridine may be the substance added; 3. **Wood**—alcohol obtained by the destructive distillation of wood (or by the synthesis of carbon monoxide and hydrogen: $CO + 2H_2 \rightarrow CH_3OH$). Wood alcohol is called methanol, or methyl alcohol. It is the simplest of all alcohols and is used in industry as antifreeze; 4. **Grain**—alcohol produced by the fermentation of starch in potatoes, rice, corn, and other grains. Grain alcohol is called ethanol, or ethyl alcohol, and is the product in wines, beers, and whisky.

A SELECTION OF ALCOHOLS

NAME	FORMULA	"PARENT" PRODUCT
Methyl alcohol	CH_3OH	CH_4
Ethyl alcohol	C_2H_5OH	C_2H_6
Propyl alcohol	C_3H_7OH	C_3H_8
Butyl alcohol	C_4H_9OH	C_4H_{10}
Amyl alcohol	$C_5H_{11}OH$	C_5H_{12}

Aldehydes A group of organic compounds formed by the oxidation of alcohols. For example, formaldehyde (HCHO) is made by adding oxygen to methanol.

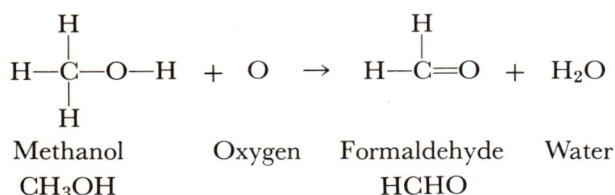

$$H-\underset{\underset{H}{|}}{\overset{\overset{H}{|}}{C}}-O-H \ + \ O \ \rightarrow \ H-\overset{\overset{H}{|}}{C}=O \ + \ H_2O$$

Methanol	Oxygen	Formaldehyde	Water
CH₃OH		HCHO	

Aliphatic Compounds Organic compounds in the form of a chain, as opposed to a ring form. Ethane (C_2H_6) is a chain, or aliphatic, compound; while benzene (C_6H_6) is a ring, or aromatic, compound.

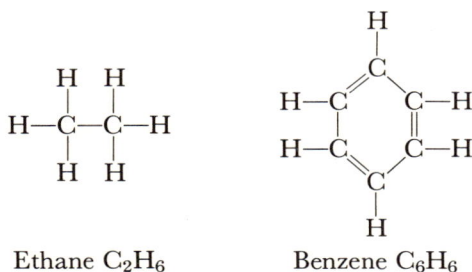

Ethane C₂H₆   Benzene C₆H₆

Alkali An exceptionally strong base. Solutions which contain lye (NaOH) and ammonia (NH₃), for example, and which turn litmus blue and neutralize acids. While acids are "proton donors," alkalies are "proton acceptors."

Searles Lake, California, is a concentrated solution of sodium chloride and other salts. The liquid brine is piped to a factory which separates the salts.

Allotropy The different forms an element or crystal may have; these differences are caused by differences in the arrangement or number of atoms making up the molecule. Ozone (O_3) is an *allotrope* of normal molecular oxygen (O_2), and has 3 instead of 2 atoms. The diamond and graphite are both *allotropic* forms of carbon, each having a different structure. (See *Diamond, Graphite.*)

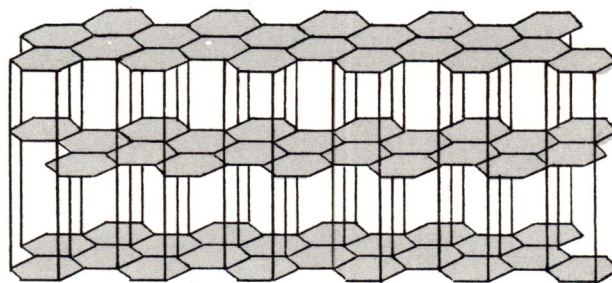

Graphite, an allotrope of carbon, is "slippery" because its atoms are arranged in layers that slide over each other. The bonds joining the layers are weak.

Alloy A metal made by mixing 2 or more different metals together; for example, bronze is an alloy made by melting copper and tin together. Aluminum bronze is a mixture of aluminum and copper. (*Table of Alloys,* p. 76.)

Alpha Particle Written α particle. The nucleus of a helium atom, having 2 neutrons and 2 protons, hence it is positively charged. These particles are given off by certain radioactive elements and travel at a speed equal to about one-fifteenth the velocity of light. They do not have a strong penetrating power; a thin sheet of metal can stop them.

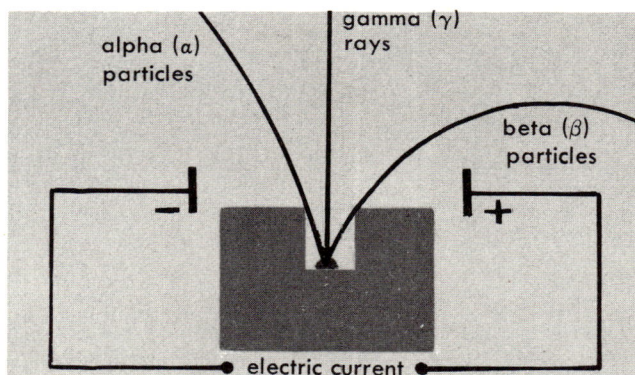

Alpha particles (α) have a positive charge, so they are attracted by the negative pole of a magnet.

Alpha Rays A stream of alpha particles.

Alum A class of crystal compounds made by combining the sulfate of a metal of valence 1^+ with the sulfate of a metal of valence 3^+. For example, common alum is potassium aluminum sulfate, written as $KAl(SO_4)_2 \cdot 12H_2O$. Common alum is used to make dyes "fast" (see *Mordant*) and for fireproofing.

A cluster of alum crystals.

Amalgam Any solid or liquid alloy that contains mercury. Dentists use amalgam alloys to fill back teeth. On hardening, the alloy expands slightly and so fills the cavity.

Amino Acids The building blocks of proteins, derived from ammonia and containing the amino group (NH_2-). The simplest amino acid is glycine—CH_2NH_2COOH. It consists of the amino group added to acetic acid (CH_3COOH). There are about 25 known amino acids.

Ammonia A strong-smelling gas—NH_3. It forms a base solution with water, and is widely used in fertilizers and explosives.

Amorphous Without any observable crystalline shape; for example, glass and flesh are amorphous substances.

Analysis Breaking down substances into their component elements. **1. Qualitative**—breaking down a material to find out the kinds of elements of which it is composed; **2. Quantitative**—breaking down a material to find out both the kinds and quantities of the elements of which it is composed. (See also *Spectroscopic Analysis*.)

Aromatic compounds, like the four shown here, have distinctive odors and are derivatives of benzene.

Anhydride (See *Acid Anhydride, Base Anhydride*.)

Anhydrous Lacking water.

Aniline $C_6H_5NH_2$. An organic compound which is the starting point for many synthetic compounds, including dyes, drugs, and plastics.

Anion Any negative ion; an anode-seeking ion, hence its name. (See *Charge*.)

Annealing Heating and then slowly cooling glass or metals. The regulated cooling prevents the glass or metal from developing strains which would result from a sudden change in temperature brought on by rapid cooling. (See *Quenching, Tempering*.)

Anode The positive electrode, where oxidation takes place. (See *Electrolysis*.)

Antifreeze A mixture of water and ethylene glycol. It is the substance usually used in automobile radiators to lower the freezing point of the water and so protect the car in cold weather.

Aqua Regia A strong acid. A mixture of concentrated hydrochloric acid (3 parts) and concentrated nitric acid (1 part); aqua regia is highly corrosive, dissolves gold.

Aromatic Compounds Organic compounds which have a distinctive odor, have a ring form, and are derivatives of benzene. (See *Benzene, Aliphatic Compounds*.)

cloves

mothballs

peppermint

thyme

9

Asbestos A hard silicate mineral (usually calcium magnesium silicate) that can be shredded into fibers and then made into cloth. The material is fireproof and makes a good insulator.

Asphalt The thick black substance found in nature (the La Brea tar pits) and left at the bottom of a fractionating tower after fractional distillation. Asphalt is used as a roofing material and for road surfacing. (See also *Fractionating Tower*.)

Animals trapped in the La Brea tar swamp, California, millions of years ago, were preserved as fossils.

Aspirin Acetyl-salicylic acid—$CH_3COOC_6H_4COOH$. A mild drug used to reduce pain nearly anywhere in the body. It is sold under a variety of names.

Atmosphere 1. The envelope of gases surrounding the earth (see *Air*); 2. A unit of pressure: normal atmospheric pressure at sea level supports a column of mercury 760 mm. high (29.92 inches) at 0°C. Normal atmospheric pressure equals 14.72 pounds per square inch.

Atom The smallest possible piece of an element that can take part in a chemical reaction. An atom retains all the properties of its element.

Atomic Number The number of protons contained in the nucleus of an atom.

Atomic Pile (See *Nuclear Reactor*.)

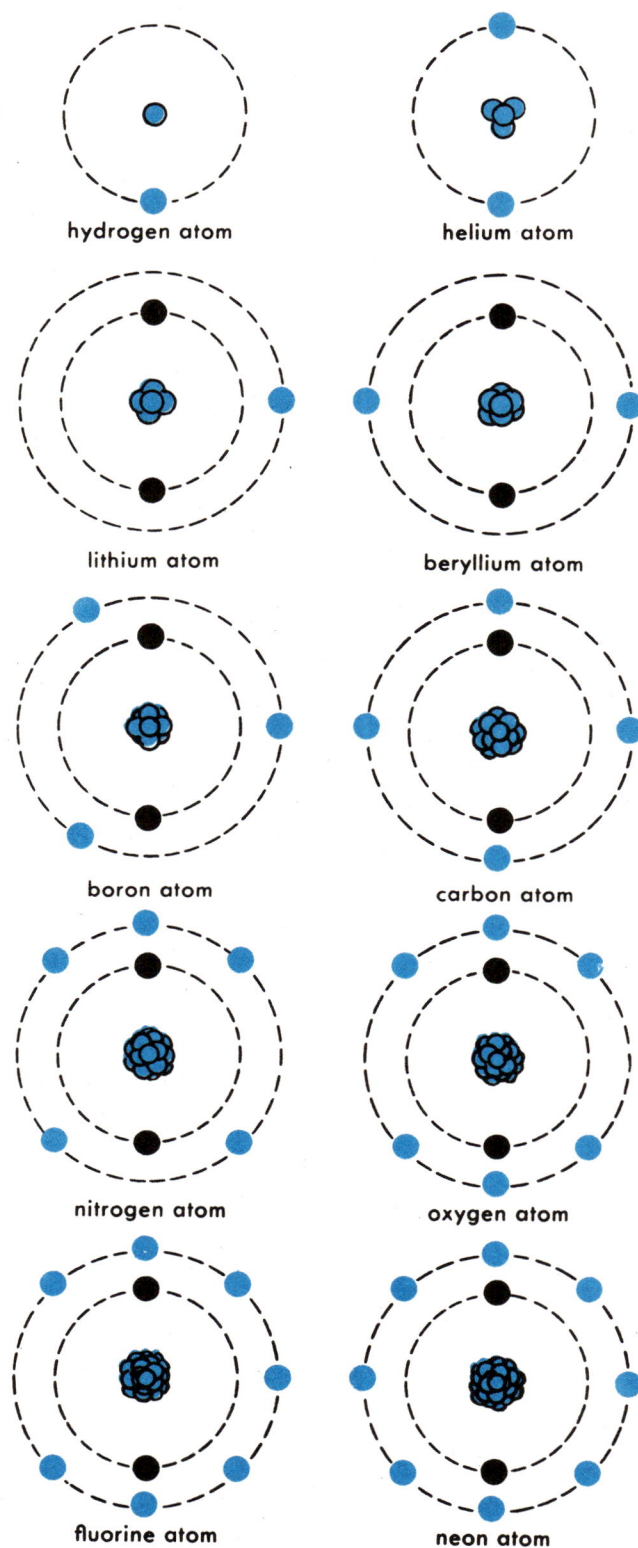

hydrogen atom   helium atom

lithium atom   beryllium atom

boron atom   carbon atom

nitrogen atom   oxygen atom

fluorine atom   neon atom

Hydrogen has the simplest atom—one proton forming the nucleus and one electron orbiting about it (top left). After hydrogen, atoms grow more complex as shown here. (See also: *Proton, Electron, Neutron, Nucleus,* and *Electron Shells.*)

Atomic Theory The idea that all matter is made up of tiny particles called "atoms"; that atoms are the smallest particles that can retain all of the properties of elements; that the atoms of the same element are all alike in weight and properties; that the atoms of different elements are not alike in weight or properties; that chemical compounds are formed when the atoms of different elements combine in simple numerical proportions (for example, 2 atoms of hydrogen combine with 1 atom of oxygen when water is formed). The atomic theory was developed by John Dalton.

Atomic Weight The weight of an atom of each element compared with a weight of 16 avograms (or atomic weight units—a.w.u.) assigned to an oxygen atom. (See *Avogram.*)

Avogadro Number 6.02×10^{23}—which is the number of molecules in 22.4 liters of a gas at standard temperature and pressure.

Avogadro's Hypothesis Equal volumes of all gases at the same temperature and pressure contain the same number of molecules.

Avogram The unit of weight expressing the actual weight of atoms. The unit is 1 gram divided by Avogadro's number, 6.02×10^{23}.

B

Babbitt Metal Alloys which contain a large amount of tin and small amounts of antimony and copper. Lead sometimes is used to replace part of the tin.

Baking Powder A mixture of baking soda with an acid material such as cream of tartar for use in leavening cakes. All baking powders release carbon dioxide when mixed in water, or when heated; hence the use of the dry powder in fire extinguishers. On contact with the flame, the powder releases carbon dioxide, which smothers the flame.

Baking Soda A white substance—sodium hydrogen carbonate—$NaHCO_3$.

Barometer An instrument used for measuring atmospheric pressure. When the atmospheric pressure is "high," a greater weight of air presses down on the surface of mercury in the vessel (see illustration); hence the column of mercury in the tube rises higher. When the atmospheric pressure is "low," a lesser weight of air presses down on the surface of mercury in the vessel, hence the column of mercury in the tube lowers. Normal, sea-level atmospheric pressure pushes the column of mercury to a height of 760 mm. (29.92 inches) when the air is 0°C.

air at high pressure   air at low pressure

Air at high pressure pushes the barometer's mercury column higher than air at low pressure does.

Base A substance that neutralizes acids by forming a salt and water. (See *Alkali.*)

Base Anhydride An oxide (such as calcium oxide—CaO) that forms a base when combined with water.

Base Metals Unlike the noble metals gold and silver, base metals such as iron and copper tarnish or corrode when exposed to air, because they are more active chemically.

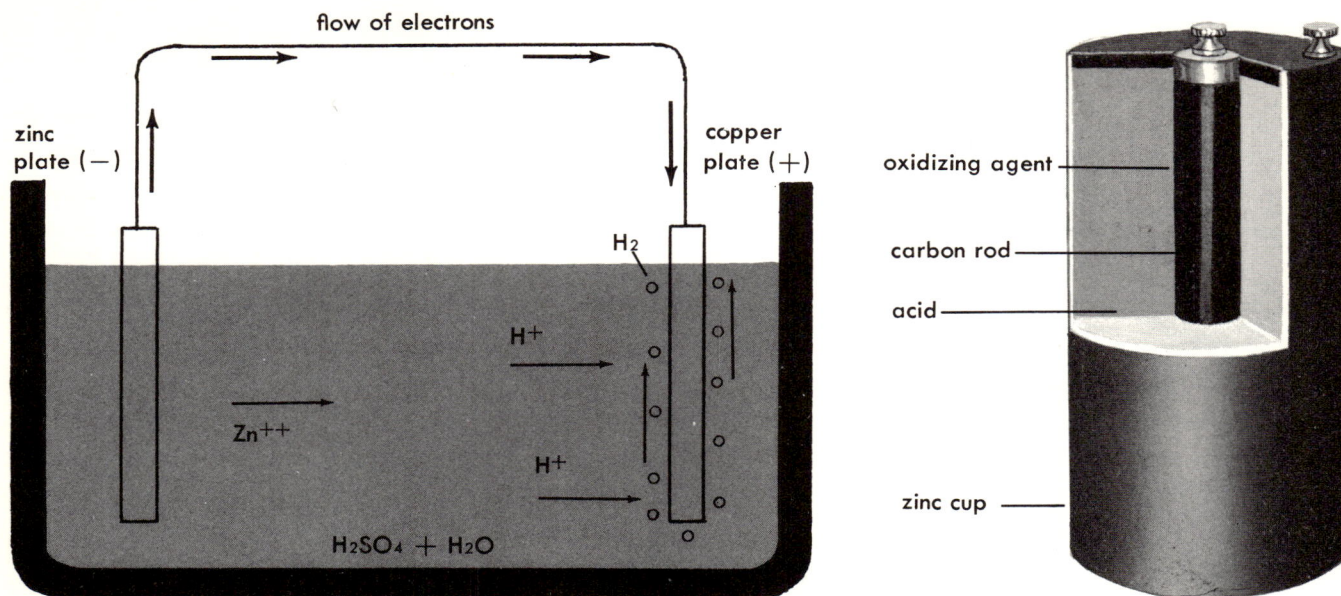

In a simple electric cell (left) and in a dry cell (right) chemical energy is changed into electrical energy.

Battery A device designed to produce an electric current by chemical means. **1. Simple Electric Cell**—a copper rod and a zinc rod placed in a dilute solution of sulfuric acid make a simple battery. The rods are called "electrodes" and the solution is called an "electrolyte." The acid attacks the metal rods in such a way that the zinc plate is given a negative charge by acquiring a surplus supply of electrons (as it loses positive zinc ions). Meanwhile, positive hydrogen ions from the solution move toward the copper plate, giving the plate a positive charge. Now electricity is simply a flow of electrons, so by connecting the two metal plates by a copper wire we can make the zinc's surplus of electrons flow through the wire to the copper plate. When electrons arrive at the plate they join with the hydrogen ions and with them form hydrogen gas which escapes (see diagram). **2. Dry Cell**—a battery used in flashlights and door bells. The cell consists of a zinc cup containing graphite manganese dioxide (the oxidizing agent), and ammonium chloride (as an acid). When the positive and negative electrodes are connected—when you switch the flashlight on—chemical reaction begins. As in the simple electric cell, the zinc becomes negatively charged and the carbon becomes positively charged; hence when the circuit is closed, electrons stream from the zinc cathode, through the bulb, to the carbon anode.

Beta particles (β) have a negative charge, so they are attracted by the positive pole of a magnet.

Bauxite A high-grade aluminum ore; a hydrated aluminum oxide—$Al_2O_3 \cdot 2H_2O$.

Benzene An organic hydrocarbon coming from coal tar. It reacts with many substances by easily giving up its hydrogen atoms (see *Derivative*) and allowing them to be replaced by other atoms or groups. Gasoline and many other substances are derivatives of benzene. Three double bonds hold the benzene ring together. Benzene and related "cyclic" hydrocarbons are called "aromatic hydrocarbons."

Beta Particles Written β particle. Electrons given off by certain radioactive elements, hence they are particles with a negative charge and are much lighter than alpha particles. Beta particles travel at about nine-tenths the speed of light. They can penetrate a thin sheet of aluminum.

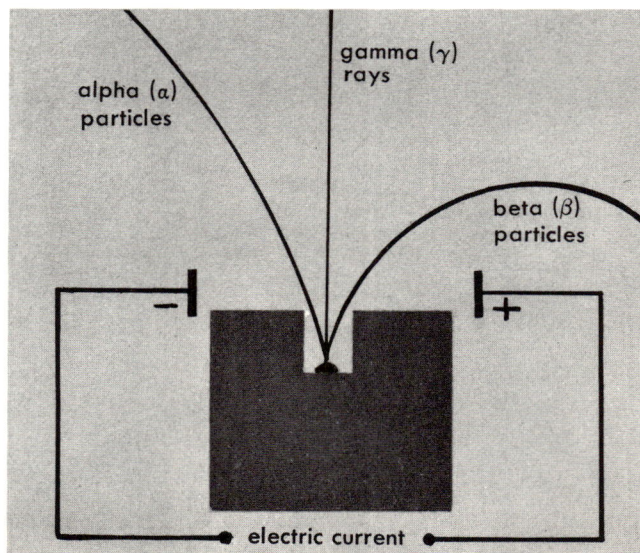

Beta Rays   A stream of beta particles.

Bicarbonate of Soda   Baking soda—$NaHCO_3$.

Binary   Meaning two. A binary compound is one made up of two elements—H_2O or $NaCl$.

Biochemistry   The chemistry of living things.

Blast Furnace   A furnace in which iron is separated from its ore. The iron ore plus coke and limestone are poured into the furnace from the top, while hot compressed air is forced in at

survive the trip to the surface, the pressure within them must be equal to the atmospheric pressure at the surface. Since the atmospheric pressure high up on a mountain is less than at sea level, liquids boil more easily at high altitudes than at low altitudes. For example, water at sea level boils at 100°C., but around 10,000 feet altitude it boils at about 90°C. Because it boils at a lower temperature, less heat passes into the food you may be trying to cook; so it takes longer to boil foods high up on a mountain than at sea level. (See also *Vapor Pressure*.)

Iron is separated from its ore in a blast furnace as the ore is mixed with coke and limestone and burned at a high temperature. Molten iron and molten slag form at the bottom of the furnace and are drawn off.

COURTESY UNITED STATES STEEL CORPORATION

iron ore
coke
limestone

200° C

480° C

1930° C

hot air → ← hot air

molten slag

molten iron

the bottom. Molten iron is separated from the slag which forms, and is cast into molds. This iron is called cast iron or pig iron. (See *Pig Iron*.)

Bleaching Agents   Chemicals which remove the color from colored textiles by changing the dyes chemically by oxidizing them (permanent), or reducing them (temporary). Four bleaching agents are: calcium hypochlorite; chlorine; hydrogen peroxide; sulfur dioxide.

Blue Vitriol   Called bluestone, it is crystalline copper sulfate—$CuSO_4 \cdot 5H_2O$.

Boiling   A liquid boils when bubbles of vapor form at the bottom of the container and rise to the top. In order for these vapor bubbles to

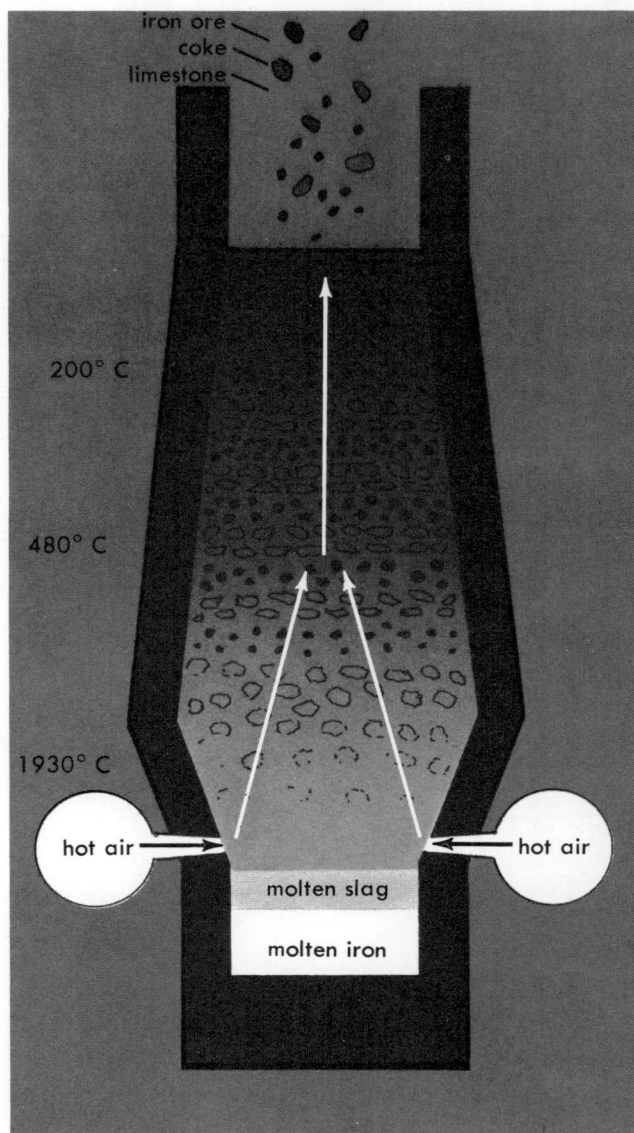

Boiling Point (b.p.) The temperature at which the vapor pressure of a liquid equals the pressure of the surrounding air, i.e., at sea level when it equals 760 mm. The result is that the liquid is changed into vapor.

Bonds (See *Chemical Bonds.*)

Borax Sodium tetraborate—$Na_2B_4O_7 \cdot 10H_2O$. A crystalline salt found in large deposits in Death Valley. It can be used as a softening agent for water (see *Hard Water*), an antiseptic, and in ceramic glazes and enamels.

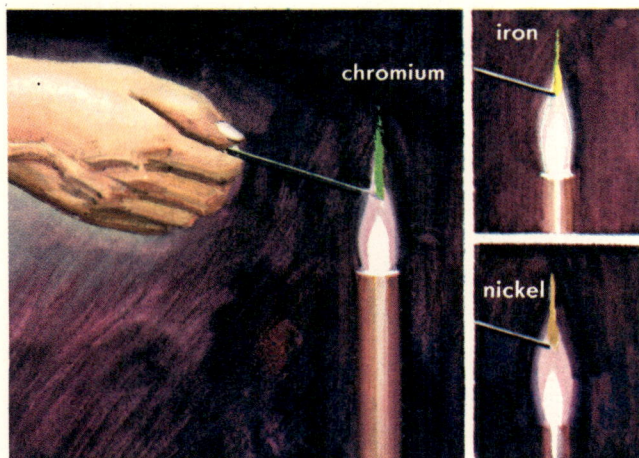

The illustration shows typical colors of three metals when held in the oxidizing flame of a Bunsen burner.

Borax Bead Test A test to identify metals making up various compounds. You can make borax beads by fusing a small amount of borax in the loop of a platinum wire. Next touch the hot bead to a speck of the compound you want to identify, then reheat the bead either in the outer (oxidizing) or inner (reducing) flame of a Bunsen burner. The following metals produce characteristic colors:

METAL	OXIDIZING FLAME	REDUCING FLAME
Chromium	Green	Green
Cobalt	Blue	Blue
Iron	Yellow	Green
Manganese	Violet	Colorless
Nickel	Brown	Colorless
Uranium	Yellow	Green

Boric Acid H_3BO_3. A mild antiseptic made from borax and occurring naturally as a white solid in volcanic regions.

Boyle's Law (See special section on *Chemical Laws,* p. 72.)

Brass An alloy made of a mixture of copper and zinc. Sometimes brass includes small amounts of tin, iron, or lead. (See also special section on *Alloys,* p. 76.)

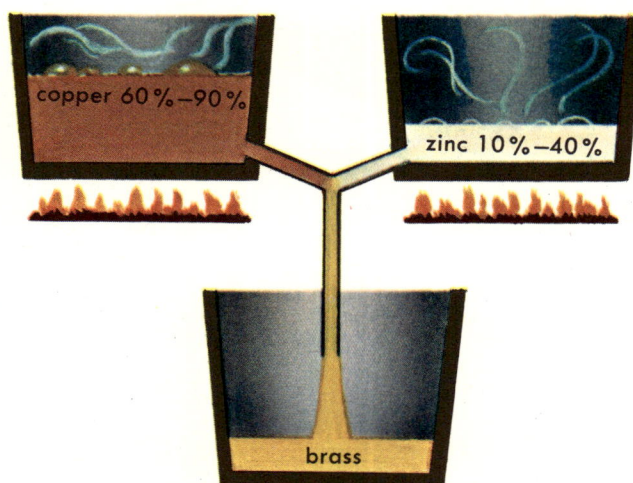

Brass, made by mixing copper and zinc, is the most important commercial alloy of copper. It is used to make jewelry, hardware, plumbing and lamp fixtures, clocks, ammunition, and many other products.

1. clay mixture ready for mold

2. clay is next pressed into a mold and dried

3. dried bricks are baked in a kiln

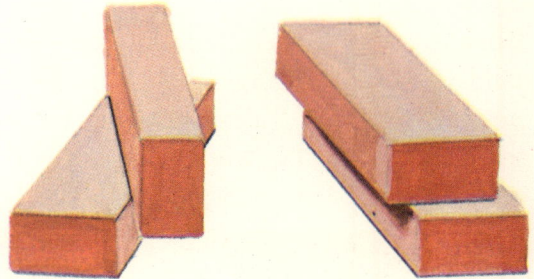
4. baked bricks ready for use

Brick The red bricks used in housebuilding are made of clay mixed with water, sand, and feldspar. The clay is pressed into molds, dried, and then baked in special ovens (called a kiln) for several days.

British Thermal Unit (B.t.u.) The amount of heat needed to raise the temperature of one pound of water 1°F. Equal to 252 calories.

Bronze An alloy made by mixing copper and tin. (See also special section on *Alloys,* p. 76.)

Brownian Motion The darting and zigzag movements of microscopic particles suspended in a liquid or in a gas. The erratic movements are caused by continuous bombardment of the particles by molecules making up the liquid or gas. Named after Robert Brown, who first observed the motion in 1828.

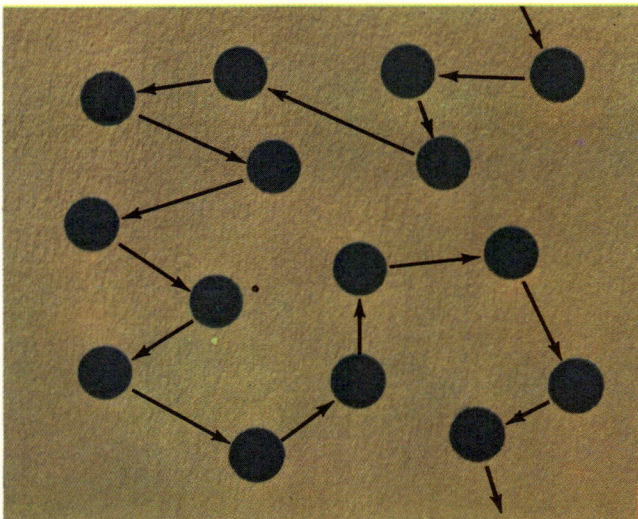

B.t.u. An abbreviation—British thermal unit.

Burning (See *Combustion.*)

Butadiene C_4H_6. An unsaturated hydrocarbon gas which is an important intermediate stage in making certain synthetic rubbers.

By-product A secondary product given off during the manufacture of a primary product. For example, when coal gas (primary product) is made, ammonia, coal tar, and coke (secondary products) are given off as by-products.

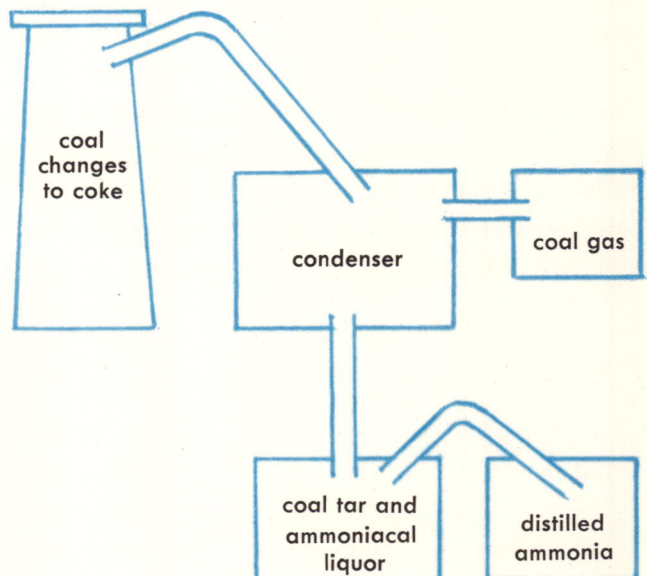

coal changes to coke

condenser

coal gas

coal tar and ammoniacal liquor

distilled ammonia

C

Calorie (cal.) The amount of heat needed to raise the temperature of 1 g. of water 1°C. To heat 2 g. of water 1°C. requires 2 cal. To heat 1 g. of water 10°C. requires 10 cal. To heat 10 g. of water 10°C. requires 100 cal. A **large Calorie** (with a capital C and called a **kilocalorie**) equals 1000 regular calories and is the unit of measure for energy values of food. (See table of *Food Values* on p. 82.)

Carbohydrate Any organic compound made up of carbon, hydrogen, and oxygen only; usually with about twice as many hydrogen atoms as carbon atoms, as in fruit sugar (levulose) $C_6H_{12}O_6$.

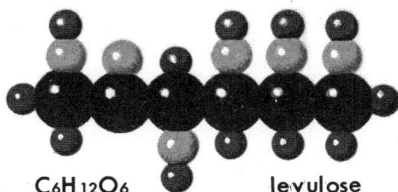

$C_6H_{12}O_6$ levulose

Carbolic Acid C_6H_5OH (phenol). A white corrosive and poisonous solid used as a disinfectant and in making dyes and plastics. When carbolic acid is heated with formaldehyde in a base solution, the plastic called "resinoid" is produced. Further heating of the resinoid changes the product to the plastic commercially known as Bakelite.

Carbonated Water Water containing carbon dioxide (CO_2) in solution. Pressure inside a bottle of soda water keeps the CO_2 dissolved, but when you reduce the pressure, by removing the cap, the CO_2 bubbles out of the solution as a gas.

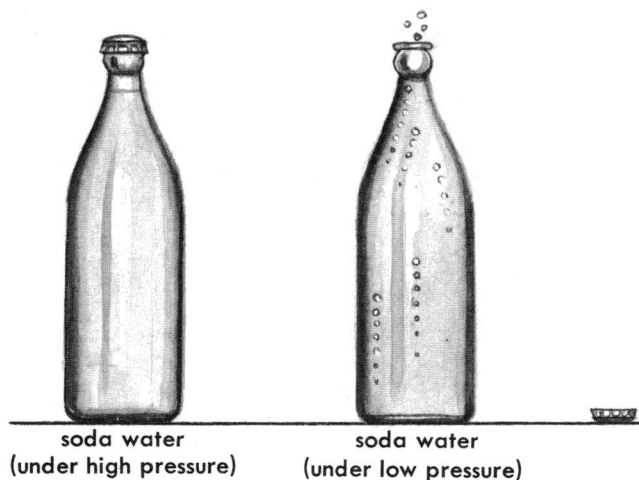

soda water
(under high pressure)

soda water
(under low pressure)

Carborundum Silicon carbide—SiC. A material used as an abrasive because of its hardness. It is nearly as hard as diamond. Carborundum is made by heating silica (SiO_2) with carbon.

Casein The major protein found in milk. It is found as a light, yellow solid when milk sours, or when milk is curdled by the addition of rennin. Casein is used in the manufacture of synthetic textile fibers, paints, paper coating, and plastics.

Cast Iron The molten iron produced when iron is separated from its ore in a blast furnace. Cast iron contains about 4% carbon plus other impurities. (See *Blast Furnace.*)

Catalyst Any chemical that speeds up or slows down the reaction between two other chemicals, without itself being altered at the end of the reaction. Positive catalysts (called *promoters*) speed up a reaction; negative catalysts (called *inhibitors*) slow down a reaction. An example of a catalyst is the enzyme ptyalin in saliva. Ptyalin helps change starch to sugar as we chew our food.

Cathode The negative electrode, where reduction takes place. (See *Electrolysis.*)

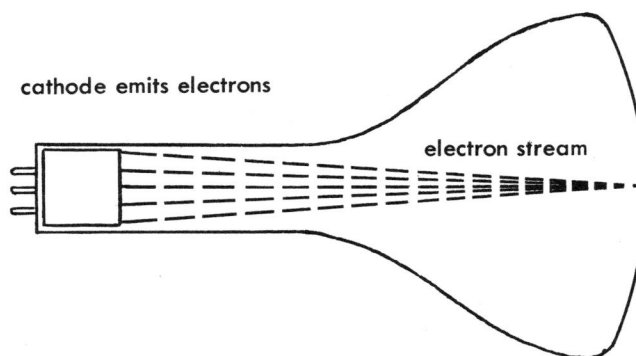

cathode emits electrons

electron stream

The image on a TV picture tube is made by a beam of electrons sweeping over the tube's inner surface.

Cathode Rays A stream of electrons given off by the cathode when an electrical discharge takes place in a vacuum tube. The picture tube in a television set is a cathode-ray tube.

Cation Any positive ion; a cathode-seeking ion, hence its name. (See *Charge*.)

Caustic Soda (See *Lye*.)

Celluloid The first synthetic plastic. It is made by combining nitrocellulose and camphor. Because Celluloid is brittle, colors with age, and is flammable, it has been replaced by more suitable plastics. (See also special section on *Plastics*, p. 84.)

Cellulose An organic compound—$(C_6H_{10}O_5)_n$. It forms the cell walls of plants and is used in the manufacture of paper, explosives, and rayon.

Cellulose comes from wood and cotton. It is used in many products . . .

Celsius Scale Official name for the Centigrade temperature scale, on which water freezes at 0° and boils at 100° at standard atmospheric pressure (760 mm.).

Cement The mixture in sand and water of limestone and clay composed of three oxides: lime (CaO); alumina (Al_2O_3); and silica (SiO_2).

Centigrade Scale On this temperature scale, water freezes at 0° and boils at 100° at standard pressure (760 mm.). To convert from Centigrade to Fahrenheit, multiply the Centigrade reading by 9, divide by 5, and add 32.

Centigram (cg.) 0.01 gram.

Centimeter (cm.) 0.01 meter. (See also *Metric System*.)

Chain Reaction An action which, when started, continues at a geometric rate. For example, we begin with a fissionable material such as uranium^{235}. To start the chain reaction we bombard the nucleus of a uranium atom with a neutron. The result is that the nucleus of the uranium atom releases two new neutrons which bombard two other uranium atoms. These two atoms release four neutrons which bombard four other uranium atoms, and so on (see diagram). A reaction of this kind produces a tremendous explosion—an atomic-bomb explosion. (This is a much oversimplified explanation. The interested reader should investigate in more detail the number of neutrons liberated when a U^{235} atom is split.)

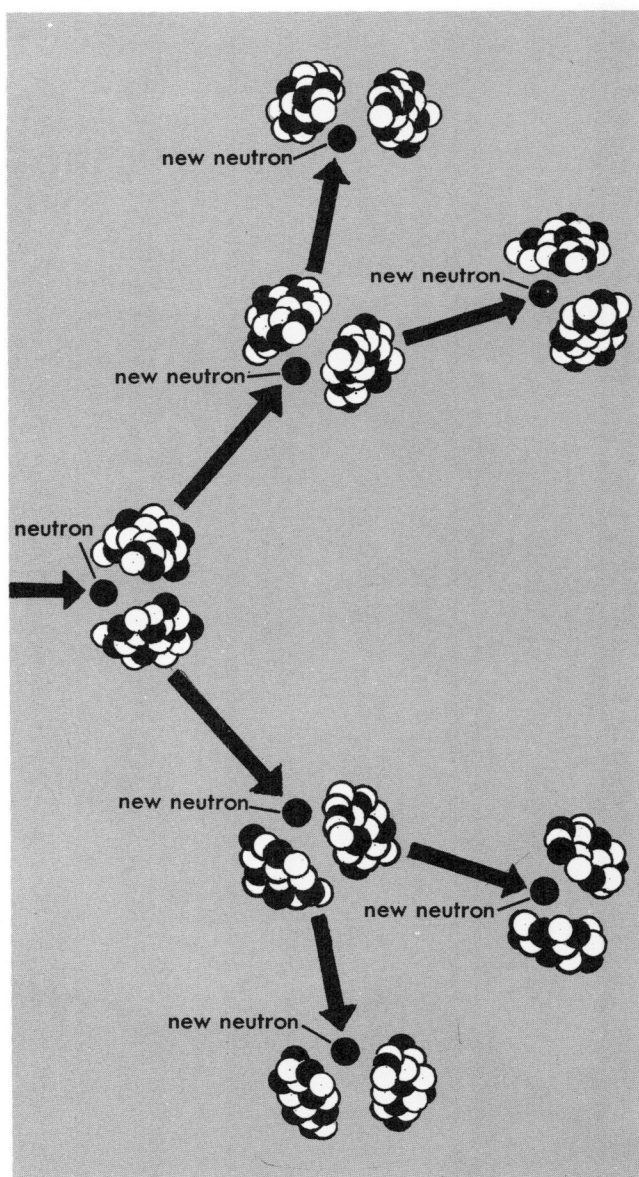

Like the Dover Cliffs, the Seven Sisters Cliffs, near Dover, were formed by dead marine animals.

Chalk Calcium carbonate formed in nature—$CaCO_3$. The famous Dover Cliffs in England are made of this natural chalk, the remains of minute marine animals that died millions of years ago. Blackboard chalk is calcium sulfate —$CaSO_4$.

Charcoal A nearly pure form of carbon. It can be made by heating wood in the absence of air. During the heating, certain by-products are given off—acetic acid, wood alcohol, and acetone. Charcoal burns without smoke and leaves little ash. (See also *Activated Charcoal*.)

Charge A neutral atom is one whose negative charge of electrons "balances" its positive charge of protons. If the atom gains electrons, it is given a negative charge. If it loses electrons, it is left with a positive charge. Such charged atoms are called ions.

Charles' Law (See special section on *Chemical Laws*, p. 72.)

Chemical Bonds The electrical forces that hold together the atoms making up a compound. Certain atoms (those of Group O in the periodic table) will not combine with atoms of other elements. The reason is that the arrangement of electrons makes them "stable"; that is, the outer electron shell has as many electrons as it can hold (see entry *Electron Shells*). These "complete" atoms in Group O are said to be inert, or inactive. Atoms whose outer shells do not have the maximum number of electrons are willing to gain electrons, lose electrons, or share electrons. In other words, they "strive" to become stable. Such atoms combine readily with other atoms and so form compounds. Here is how they do it: **1. Electrovalent Bonds**—an atom such as sodium (with one electron in its outer shell) lends this electron to an atom of chlorine, which has 7 electrons in its outer shell. The result is that the sodium acquires a positive charge (by giving up its electron) and the chlorine atom acquires a negative charge (by

The carbon (C) atoms in the compounds shown below are held together by sharing electrons (covalent bonds)— in single bonds (ethane and octane), double bonds (ethylene and benzene), and triple bonds (acetylene).

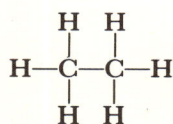

Ethane C_2H_6
single bond

Acetylene C_2H_2
triple bond

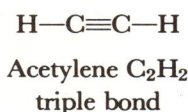

Ethylene C_2H_4
double bond

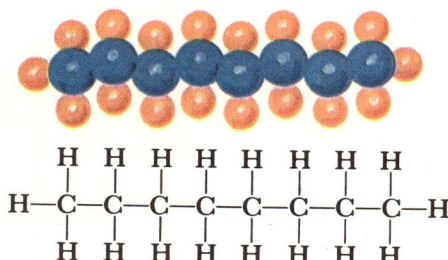

Normal octane C_8H_{18}
straight chain

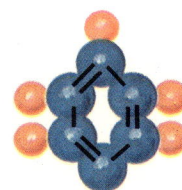
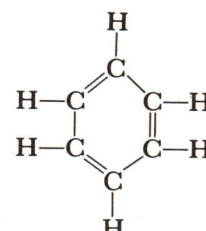

Benzene C_6H_6
ring compound

gaining the electron). The two atoms are now held together by an electrical bond. The molecule of ordinary salt (NaCl) is held together this way. **2. Covalent Bonds**—the bonds that are formed when two neutral atoms, such as hydrogen and chlorine, share a pair of electrons, each atom contributing one electron to the pair. Both hydrochloric acid (HCl) and water (H_2O) are bonded this way. **3. Co-ordinate Covalent Bonds**—the bonds that are formed when both electrons shared in the pair come from one atom. (See also *Polar Bond.*)

1. Combination

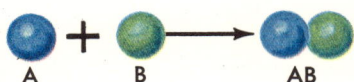

2. Decomposition

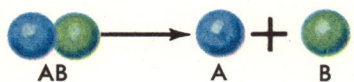

3. Displacement

4. Double decomposition

Chemical Change A change in the arrangement of atoms of a substance by chemical means, resulting in a new substance. **1. Combination**—when two substances combine and form a new substance, $A + B \rightarrow AB$; example: $2H_2 + O_2 \rightarrow 2H_2O$. **2. Decomposition**—when one substance is broken down into its component parts; the opposite of simple combination, $AB \rightarrow A + B$; example: $2H_2O \rightarrow 2H_2 + O_2$. **3. Displacement**—when one kind of atom takes the place of another, rather like a substitute in an athletic contest, $A + BC \rightarrow AC + B$; example: $Zn + CuSO_4 \rightarrow ZnSO_4 + Cu$. **4. Double Decomposition**—when there is an exchange of partners, such as two couples changing partners during a dance, $AB + CD \rightarrow AC + BD$; example: $CaO + 2HCl \rightarrow CaCl_2 + H_2O$.

Chemical Equilibrium ·Some chemical reactions fail to go to completion. While the two substances intended to react are combining into two new substances, the two new substances recombine and change back into the original substance. When the new substances are reacting at the same rate as the original substance, the state of equilibrium is reached. Example: Substances A and B are mixed and form substances C and D. Equilibrium is reached as shown in the equation $A + B \rightleftharpoons C + D$. Now if we remove either substance D or C as it is being formed, then A and B will continue to react until their supply is exhausted. In the laboratory we can demonstrate this condition by passing steam over red-hot iron, $4H_2O + 3Fe \rightleftharpoons Fe_3O_4 + 4H_2$. Now if we remove the hydrogen as it is formed during the reaction, the reaction goes to completion, $4H_2O + 3Fe \rightarrow Fe_3O_4 + 4H_2\uparrow$. (For another kind of equilibrium, see *Vapor Pressure.*)

Chemical Reaction When two or more substances combine and, through their rearrangement of atoms, produce a new substance. For example, when an atom of carbon combines with 2 atoms of oxygen and produces carbon dioxide (CO_2).

Chemiluminescence Certain chemical reactions produce light with very little accompanying heat. For example, the glow of fireflies.

Like the firefly, many other organisms, plants among them, have a chemical lighting system. Exactly how these systems work is not completely understood.

Chemistry The study of all substances—how they are composed, how they change, and the effects they have on one another.

Chlorination of Water The fifth and last stage in the process of purifying water for drinking. A small amount of chlorine gas, which is poisonous, is added to the water to kill bacteria. Although the amount used is harmful to bacteria, it is not harmful to man. (See *Water Purification* diagram.)

Chloroform An anesthetic—$CHCl_3$. A sweet-smelling, heavy, colorless liquid. It can be made by combining acetone, acetaldehyde, or ethyl alcohol with bleaching powder; or by combining chlorine with methane.

Chlorophyll The green coloring in plants. At least two kinds are known: $C_{55}H_{72}O_5N_4Mg$ (called chlorophyll-a) and $C_{55}H_{70}O_6N_4Mg$ (called chlorophyll-b). Chlorophyll acts as a catalyst in the process of photosynthesis. It is the chemical agent making it possible for green plants to convert carbon dioxide from the air with water from the soil and turn these substances into sugar and oxygen. (See *Photosynthesis*.)

Coal A carbon compound formed about 500 million years ago by the decay of plants packed under mud and sand. **1. Anthracite**—hard coal with a high carbon content and relatively few hydrocarbons. **2. Bituminous**—soft coal with a relatively high percentage of hydrocarbons; more widely used than anthracite for heating and power.

Coal Gas A fuel gas at one time widely used in street lights, and now used in gas stoves for cooking. It is obtained by the destructive distillation of coal and contains about 50% hydrogen (H), 35% methane (CH_4), 6% carbon monoxide (CO), 5% nitrogen (N), 3% ethylene (C_2H_4), 1% acetylene (C_2H_2).

perfume

drugs

photo chemicals

Coal Tar A thick, black liquid used for surfacing roads. It is obtained by the destructive distillation of coal. When tar is distilled, it yields creosote, pitch, and several other useful products. Coal tar is also an important source of drugs and dyes.

Cohesion The force of attraction between molecules that holds liquids and solids together. By raising the temperature of the solid or liquid, cohesion is reduced.

Coal was formed millions of years ago by the decay of plants packed under mud. Map shows coal areas.

Coke When bituminous coal is cooked in an oven (in the absence of oxygen) for about 18 hours at 2500°F., it does not burn, but decomposes. One of the products of decomposition is coke, a hard, porous solid containing about 80% carbon. Coke is important in the manufacture of iron and steel. When heated, coke provides the carbon monoxide (CO) which reduces iron ore to metallic iron. Coke is also used in the manufacture of water gas, graphite, and carborundum.

$$2C + O_2 \rightarrow 2CO$$
$$Fe_2O_3 + 3CO \rightarrow 2Fe + 3CO_2$$

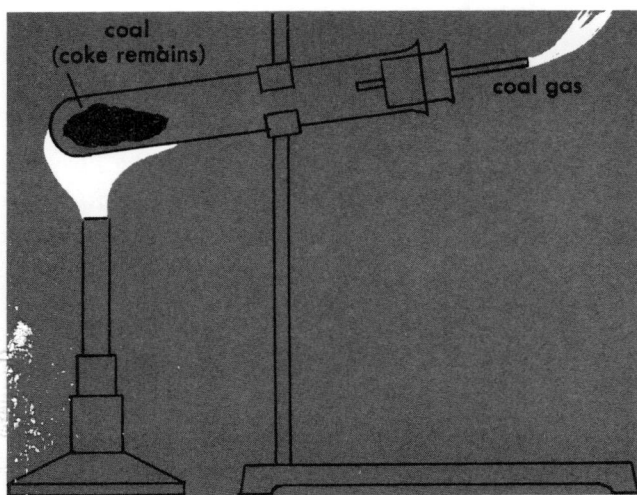

coal (coke remains)

coal gas

Colloidal State A "twilight" state of matter. Colloidal particles are larger than molecules but too small to be seen with an ordinary microscope. Colloids consist of groups of particles suspended in a gaseous, solid, or liquid medium, such as clay in water. Although the individual particles cannot be seen with a regular microscope, they can be observed as dancing pinpoints of light (see *Brownian Motion*)

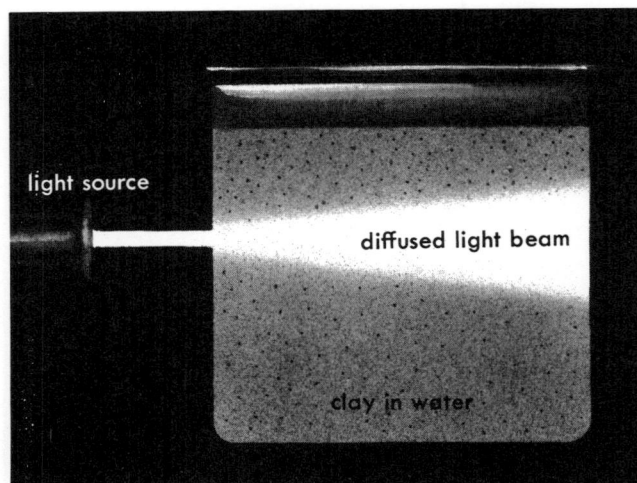

light source

diffused light beam

clay in water

when a finely focused beam of light is passed through the solution. This effect is known as the "Tyndall Effect." It is somewhat like the path of light you see in a motion-picture theater, as light from the projector strikes and illuminates smoke and dust particles in the air on its way to the screen. Certain crystals placed in a grinding mill can be ground to colloidal size (particles as small as 0.01 microns). Colloidal particles are used for making paint pigments, dyeing, and filler for paper. Some typical colloids: whipped cream (gas bubbles suspended in a liquid), salad dressing (liquid droplets suspended in a liquid), clouds (liquid droplets suspended in a gas), butterfly wings (solid particles suspended in a solid), smoke (solid particles suspended in gas).

Combining Number (See *Valence.*)

Combining Volume The volume ratios at which gases combine. For example, 2 liters of hydrogen combine with 1 liter of oxygen and produce 2 liters of water vapor. One liter of hydrogen combines with 1 liter of chlorine and produces 2 liters of hydrochloric-acid gas.

Combining Weight (Also **equivalent weight.**) 1. The atomic weight of an element divided by its valence (combining number). The combining weight of chlorine—with a valence of 1— equals its atomic weight; that of oxygen—with a valence of 2—is one-half its atomic weight. 2. The combining weight of a compound is its molecular weight divided by the total positive valence of the metallic, or positive, part of the compound. For example, the combining weight of Na_2SO_4 is 71. Divide the compound's molecular weight of 142 ($Na_2 = 46 + S = 32 + O_4 = 64 = 142$) by the total positive valence of the metal sodium—which is 2: $142 \div 2 = 71$.

Combustion Rapid oxidation. When a substance combines with oxygen at such a rate that it gives off light and heat, it is said to be "burning."

Colloidal particles are seen in a fine beam of light shining through a clay-water solution. The spreading of the light is called the "Tyndall Effect."

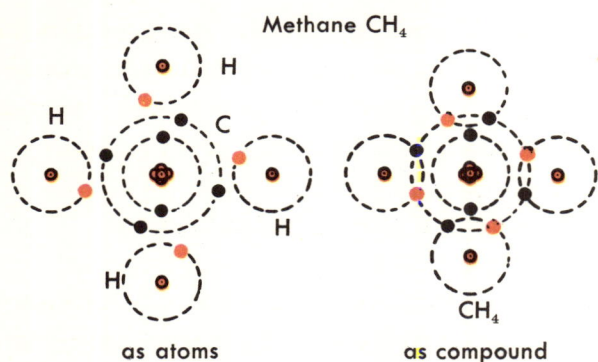

Methane CH₄

H
H   C
H
H'

as atoms

CH₄

as compound

Compound   Any substance made up of two or more elements joined chemically in definite proportions by weight. Two parts of hydrogen joined with one part of oxygen produce the compound water (H_2O).

Concentrated Solution   A solution containing a large amount of solute (acid, for example) per given amount of solvent (water, for example). The strongest acid is any concentrated acid. Mixed with water, the acid becomes weaker, or dilute.

Concentration   The concentration of a solution is the number of grams of a substance (solute) dissolved in 1000 g. of water.

Concrete   A building material made by mixing cement with sand and/or gravel and water.

Condensation   The change of a gas or vapor into a liquid. Water vapor in the air of a warm room condenses on the glass of a cold window, producing water droplets. In organic chemistry, condensation means bringing together compounds to produce a large molecule. (See also *Polymerization.*)

The water vapor in warm, moist air changes (condenses) into tiny water droplets against a cold window. (Inset shows drops enlarged.)

Conservation of Mass   According to this chemical law, there can be no change in weight in any chemical change. "Matter can be neither created nor destroyed." You can prove this statement by the following laboratory experiment: carefully weigh given quantities of silver nitrate and hydrochloric acid, then mix them in a flask. They react and form a white precipitate which weighs exactly the same as the two original substances. There are exactly the same number of atoms in the new substance as in the two original ones, and their weights have not changed, although they have gone into new combinations. Also, weigh a photo flash bulb before and then after it has been used. Although a chemical reaction takes place when the bulb flashes, there is no change in weight.

Coolant   In a nuclear reactor, the substance that transfers heat from the reactor to the heat exchanger which turns water into steam. Molten sodium can be used as a coolant. (See *Nuclear Reactor.*)

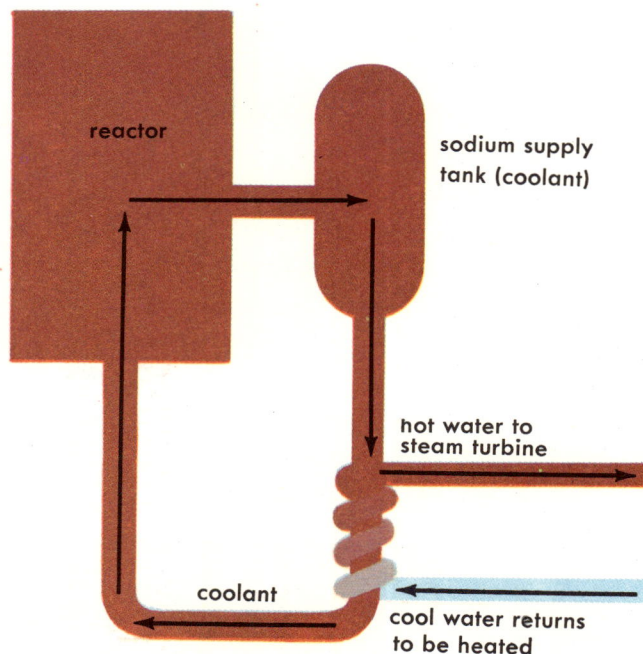

reactor

sodium supply tank (coolant)

hot water to steam turbine

coolant

cool water returns to be heated

Corrosion   A chemical reaction that takes place on the surface of certain metals exposed to air, moisture, or chemical vapors such as salt in sea air. (See also *Rust.*)

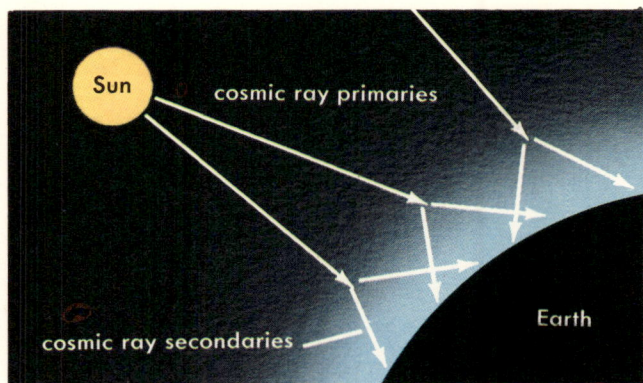

At a distance of about 25 miles above the earth, cosmic ray primaries break up and form secondaries.

Cosmic Rays High-speed subatomic particles originating in space and quite likely from the sun. They can penetrate three feet of lead or three thousand feet of water. When **Cosmic-Ray Primaries** enter the earth's atmosphere they break up into harmless **Secondary** particles which reach us at ground level. The atmosphere protects us from the harmful primaries.

Cottrell Process A method of reducing industrial smoke. As the smoke particles rise up the chimney they are charged by a high-voltage wire. When they reach a certain level in the chimney, they are attracted to a plate carrying the opposite electric charge. Once on the plate, the particles lose their charge and fall down the chimney under their own weight. As well as ridding residential areas of smoke from industry,

the Cottrell process enables by-products of smoke to be recovered. For example, arsenic oxide (used in insecticides) and potash (used in fertilizers) are both recovered from smoke.

Covalent Bond (See *Chemical Bonds*.)

Cracking Decomposing a chemical substance by high heat and pressure. In the petroleum industry cracking breaks the long chain molecules of kerosene into smaller ones, producing gasoline.

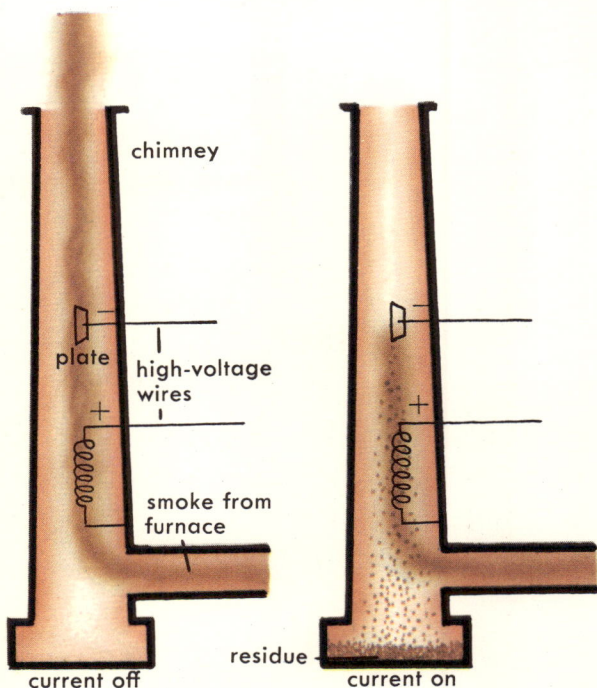

cracking tower

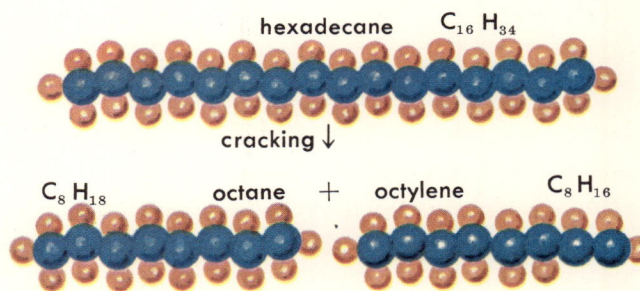

hexadecane $C_{16}H_{34}$

cracking ↓

C_8H_{18} octane + octylene C_8H_{16}

Cream of Tartar Potassium hydrogen tartrate—$KHC_4H_4O_6$. (See *Baking Powder*.)

Creosote A product obtained by distilling tar. Used for preserving wood. Railway ties and the bottom of telephone poles and fence posts are painted with creosite. (See *Coal Tar*.)

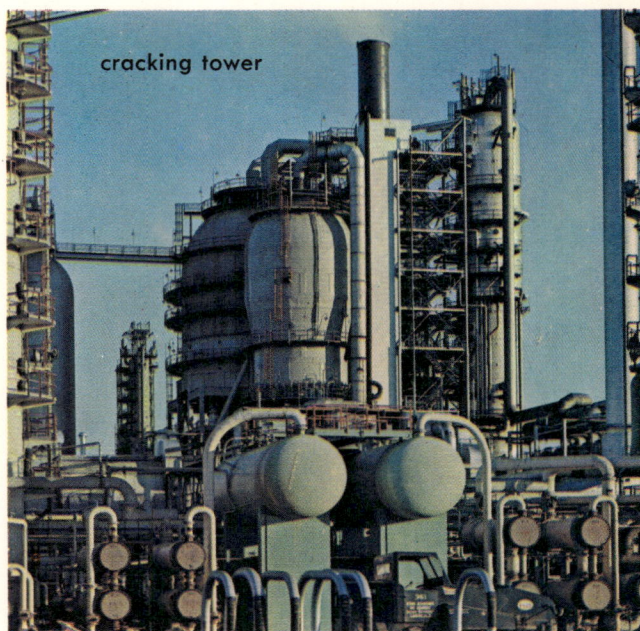

chimney

plate

high-voltage wires

smoke from furnace

residue

current off   current on

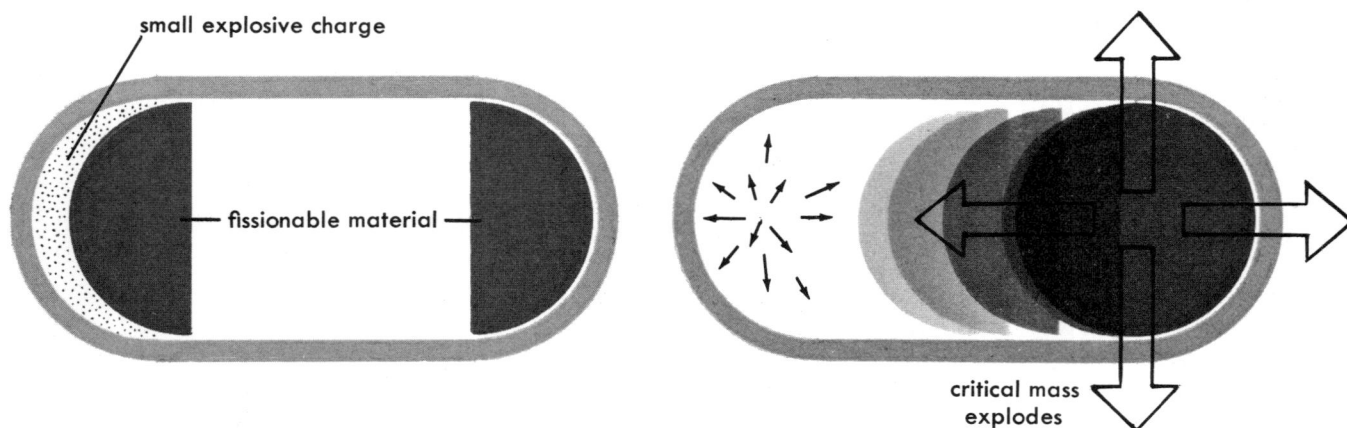

Atomic bomb: The small explosive charge combines the two blocks of fissionable material, which in turn explode.

Critical Mass   The quantity of fissionable material needed for a chain reaction to take place. In an atomic bomb there are two lumps of fissionable material, but neither one is large enough to set up a chain reaction (explode). As long as the two lumps are kept apart, too many neutrons escape from their surface to set up the reaction. But when they are joined, enough neutrons remain within the bigger lump to start the chain reaction. The size of the lump, big enough to allow a chain reaction, is called the critical mass. (See *Chain Reaction.*)

Critical Pressure   The pressure of a saturated vapor at the critical temperature.

Critical Temperature   The temperature above which a saturated vapor cannot be condensed by pressure alone.

How to Grow Sugar Crystals

You can see the form that sugar crystals have by "growing" your own crystals on a string.

Heat a pan of water on the stove until the water boils. Next turn the flame down and stir in some sugar little by little. Keep adding sugar until no more will dissolve. (This may take three or more cups.) When this stage in reached, pour some of the liquid into a warmed glass jar.

Now tie a piece of cotton string to a pencil, weight the bottom end of the string with a paper clip, and hang the string in the liquid with the pencil resting across the top of the glass.

Keep the glass in a warm place for a few days, and examine it each day. After a while you will find that you have a group of crystals "grown" on the string. Try growing the crystals in a warm place, then try growing them in a cool place. How do the crystals differ? It may take a week or two before your crystals reach the size of small rice grains.

Critical Volume   The volume of 1 g. of a substance at critical temperature and critical pressure.

Crown Glass   Glass which has barium or potassium instead of sodium. Used in telescopes and other optical instruments. (See also *Glass.*)

Cryolite   Sodium aluminum fluoride—Na_3AlF_6. Used in aluminum production.

Crystal   Any solid, three-dimensional substance bounded by planes—quartz, diamond. Pure solid substances are usually in crystalline form.

Crystalline   Any substance containing crystals. Crystalline means the opposite of amorphous. (See *Crystal.*)

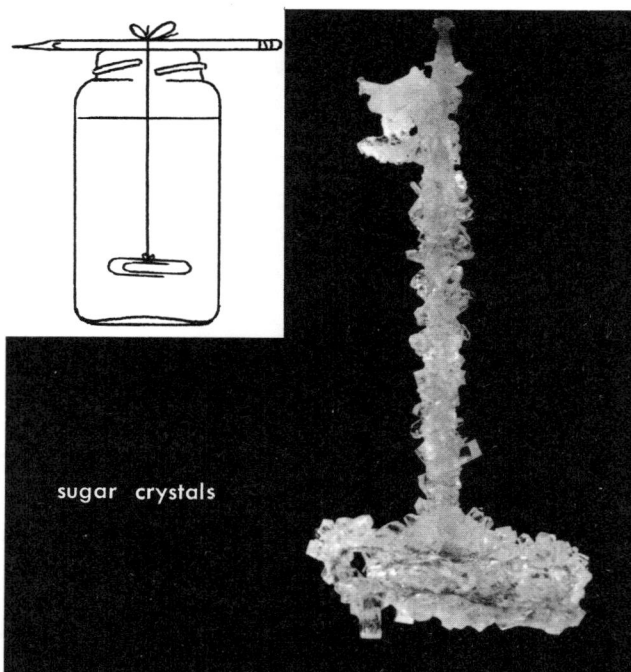

sugar crystals

PHOTO BY LEON O. BAILEY

Crystallization The process of building up crystals from a solution, determined by the solution's temperature and the rate of evaporation. High temperatures and fast evaporation produce small crystals. Low temperatures and slow evaporation produce large crystals. Try growing some crystals by: 1. placing drops of ammonium-chloride solution on a glass slide—colorless crystals will form; 2. placing drops of filtered sodium-chloride solution (rather concentrated) on a glass slide—colorless, cubical crystals will form.

Curie A unit of measure of the activity of radioactive substances. A curie is the quantity of a radioactive isotope that decays at the rate of 3.7×10^{10} disintegrations per second.

Cyclotron An apparatus that can accelerate positively charged particles (protons) by whirling them in a magnetic field. The cyclotron in the diagram consists of an evacuated metal container. Inside it are two D-shaped, hollow "boxes" which act as electrodes—one positive, one negative. Such an electric oscillator can alternate its charge extremely rapidly. If we want to accelerate protons and make them strike a target, here is what happens: At the ion source (a proton is a positive ion) hydrogen gas attacked by an electric discharge produces protons. Since the proton is positively charged, it is attracted to the "dee" that has a negative charge and is guided in a circular path by the magnetic field. When the proton reaches the gap between the two dees, the dees change their charge (polarity), so the proton continues along its path and is accelerated again. The successively changing polarity of the dees accelerates the proton twice during each trip it makes around the circuit. Very quickly the proton reaches almost the speed of light. As its speed increases, it spirals outward, finally escaping the evacuated chamber through a foil window and striking a selected target. With the cyclotron, physicists of the twentieth century can change the composition of many of the lighter chemical elements, producing a wide variety of artificial radioactive isotopes.

The Brookhaven (New York) cosmotron. The proton "gun" (foreground) shoots protons into the giant doughnut-shaped magnet, where they approach the speed of light (see text and inset). Next they are fired at atomic targets.

source of protons

dee

dee

target   foil window

D

Dacron (See special section on *Synthetic Fibers*, p. 78.)

DDT Dichloro-Diphenyl-Trichloro-ethane. An insecticide made from coal tar.

Decigram (dg.) 0.1 gram.

Decimeter (dm.) 0.1 meter.

Decomposition The breaking down of a substance into its component parts. This occurs when atoms of two or more substances forming a compound break their bonds and return to the state of elements. For example, when the hydrogen and oxygen atoms linked in the form of water break their bonds and become simply oxygen and hydrogen gas. $2H_2O \rightarrow 2H_2 + O_2$

Dehydration The removal of water from a substance. Milk is dehydrated when its water content is removed, leaving a powder.

Dehydrated, 32 ounces of milk yield 3.2 ounces of powder; 1 pound of potatoes reduces to about 3 ounces of powder; 1 onion to about ¼ ounce.

Deliquescent If a substance picks up moisture from the air and becomes sticky, or if it picks up enough moisture so that it dissolves, it is said to be deliquescent. Because calcium chloride ($CaCl_2$) is deliquescent, it is used to lay down dust on dirt roads and tennis courts. A thin film of it absorbs so much water vapor from the air that it dampens the dirt. (See also *Hygroscopic*.)

Denatured (See *Alcohol*.)

Density The amount of matter contained in a given volume, expressed as weight per unit volume. Density is expressed as the relationship between the weight of a given volume of matter and an equal volume of water. For example, a cubic foot of water weighs 62.5 pounds, and a cubic foot of mercury weighs about 845 pounds. Giving water a value of 1, the density of mercury is 13.5 g. per cubic centimeter. The mean density of the earth is about 5.5 g. per cubic centimeter, meaning that it weighs about 5½ times as much as an equal volume of water. (See also *Specific Gravity*.)

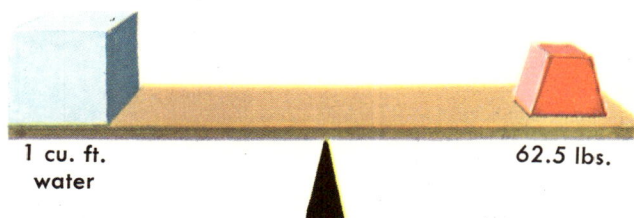

1 cu. ft. water — 62.5 lbs.

1 cu. ft. platinum — 1343.75 lbs.

DENSITY OF SOME COMMON SUBSTANCES
(in grams per cubic centimeter)

Substance	Density	Substance	Density
Cork	0.25	Magnesium	1.74
Soft wood	0.4–0.7	Aluminum	2.70
Gasoline	0.68–0.72	Glass	2.4–4.5
Hard wood	0.7–1.1	Iron	7.1–7.9
Kerosene	0.80	Copper	8.93
Ice	0.917	Silver	10.5
Distilled water	1.00	Lead	11.4
Sea water	1.03	Gold	19.3
Milk	1.03	Platinum	21.5

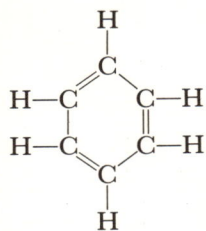

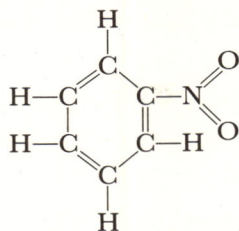

Benzene C$_6$H$_6$ Nitrobenzene C$_6$H$_5$NO$_2$

Derivative   The substance resulting from an addition to a parent substance. For example, nitrobenzene is a derivative of benzene. Benzene (C$_6$H$_6$) is the parent substance, and the nitro (—NO$_2$) group is the substance added.

Desiccator   A piece of laboratory equipment used for drying substances. It has an airtight cover and may contain a hygroscopic (drying) substance, usually calcium chloride or silica gel, which absorbs moisture from the air inside the container.

Destructive Distillation   Heating coal or wood in the absence of air and obtaining a variety of by-products. (See *Coal, Coal Gas, Coal Tar, Coke.*) The destructive distillation of wood produces wood gas, wood tar, and an aqueous layer of water, acetic acid, acetone, and wood alcohol.

Detergent   A cleaning agent. The newer detergents have calcium and magnesium salts which are soluble, which means that the detergent can be used in hard water or in sea water and will not form a scum. These detergents make water "wetter" by giving it a high penetrating power.

Deuterium   Heavy hydrogen; an isotope of hydrogen having a neutron, in addition to a proton, in the nucleus. It has an atomic weight of 2. Deuterium Oxide (D$_2$O) occurs in ordinary water and is called "heavy water." (See *Heavy Water.*)

Deuteron   The nucleus of a deuterium atom.

Developer   The photographic chemical used to reduce the silver chloride (AgCl) or silver bromide (AgBr) contained in the "emulsion" of the film. The developer leaves a black deposit of metallic silver particles on those sections of the film receiving the most light. This explains why a negative has a reversed image. (See also *Fixing.*)

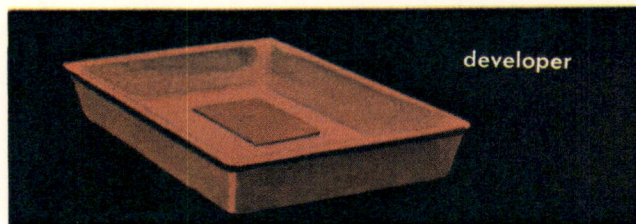

developer

water

hypo

During processing, film is bathed in developer, washed in water, then in hypo which dissolves the remaining silver salts and prevents the negative turning dark.

Dextrin A mixture of gummy carbohydrates (called dextrin) produced when starch is partly hydrolized. Dextrin is the sticky substance on the back of postage stamps, envelopes, and on the crust of pastry products.

Dextrose (See *Glucose*.)

Diamond An allotrope of carbon occurring in a crystalline form; the hardest known substance. Diamond is not affected by acids, but around 800°C. it combines with oxygen (burns) and forms carbon dioxide (CO_2). X rays pass through true diamonds, but not through artificial ones. In the diamond, each atom is bonded by four neighboring atoms. (See also *Graphite* and *Allotropy*.)

Diatomic Having two atoms. Oxygen gas (O_2) is diatomic because it has two atoms making up a molecule.

Dichloro-Diphenyl-Trichloro-ethane The reader is asked to apply his sense of humor and deductive powers to figure out what this very common substance is. It is listed under its more common name elsewhere in this glossary.

Diffusion An even spreading of one substance throughout another; as the odor of perfume in a room. All gases diffuse within a container, no matter how large the container. Sugar dissolved in water diffuses. (See also *Gaseous State*.)

Dilute Solution A solution containing a large amount of solvent (water, for example) per given amount of solute (acid, for example). A small amount of acid added to a large amount of water produces a dilute solution of the acid. Laboratory dilute solutions of acids are usually of 2 gram-equivalents per liter strength.

Dipolar Compounds (See *Polar Bond*.)

Displacement When a more active element replaces a less active one from a compound. For example, fluorine replaces chlorine locked in the compound NaCl (sodium chloride): $F_2 + 2NaCl \rightarrow 2NaF + Cl_2$. This is also known as *Replacement*.

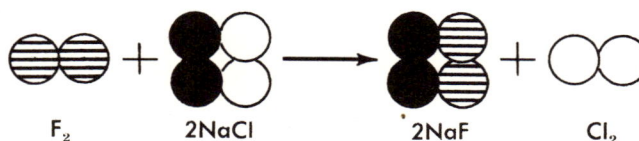

F_2 2NaCl   2NaF Cl_2

Dissociation The separation of parts of a molecule by physical means. When a molecule breaks apart. For example, at high altitudes ultraviolet rays dissociate, or break, molecular oxygen (O_2) into atomic oxygen (O). When heated, ammonium chloride (NH_4Cl) decomposes into ammonia (NH_3) and hydrogen chloride (HCl).

Distillate Any liquid product resulting from distillation.

Distillation The process of heating a liquid so that it becomes a vapor, then condensing the

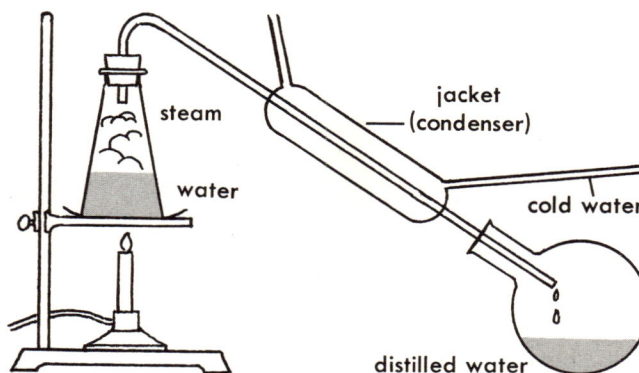

vapor so that it collects as a liquid. If a solution containing liquids of different boiling points is distilled, each liquid will be distilled off in its order of lowest boiling point. (See also *Fractionating Tower*.)

Double Bond When two electron pairs are shared in joining two atoms in a compound. (See *Benzene, Chemical Bonds, Valence*.)

Double Displacement The action that takes place when two elements present in two compounds displace one another and give rise to two new compounds. For example, in the reaction $NaCl + AgNO_3 \rightarrow AgCl + NaNO_3$, the sodium (Na) displaces the silver in the $AgNO_3$, and silver displaces the sodium in the NaCl. (See also *Displacement* and *Chemical Reaction*.)

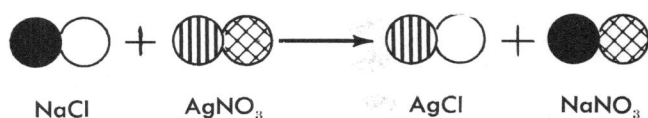

NaCl   AgNO₃   AgCl   NaNO₃

Dry Cell (See *Battery*.)

Dry Ice Solid carbon dioxide—CO_2. It has a temperature of $-78°C$. and is used as a refrigerant.

Ductility The physical state of a substance, especially metal, that allows the substance to be drawn out into a wire. Copper and silver are both ductile metals.

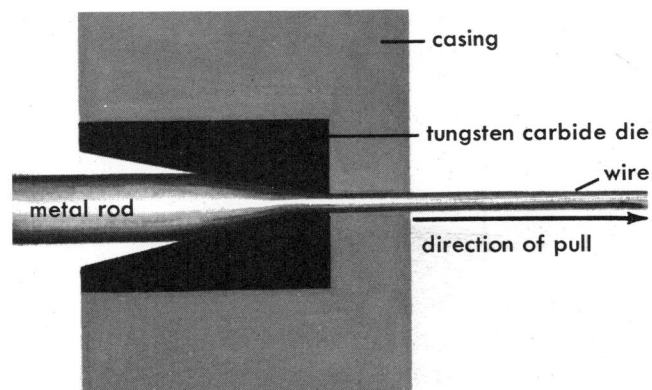

Ductile metal rods of copper and silver can be forced through a narrow opening and drawn out as fine wire.

FOUR SOURCES OF NATURAL DYES

cutch (brown and olive)

Murex trunculus (Tyrian purple)

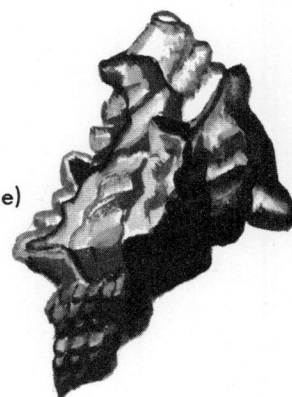

indigo plant (indigo)

butternut hulls (brown)

Dyes A group of natural compounds (about 100) or artificial compounds (more than 5000) used to color fabrics and other substances. Early natural dyes came from plants and animals— indigo from the indigo plant; Turkey red from the madder root; Tyrian purple from shellfish. Mauve was the first artificial dye and comes from coal tar. Natural dyes usually wash out of a fabric or "run," but artificial dyes usually remain "fast." (See also *Mordant*.)

E

Effervescence   The rapid escape of dissolved gases from a solution, resulting in foaming or bubbling, as in carbonated water.

Efflorescence   The action that takes place when certain crystalline salts lose their water of crystallization. The water molecules attached to the salt are so loose that they become detached, leaving the salt a dry powder. For example, crystals of washing soda ($Na_2CO_3 \cdot 10H_2O$) readily give up their water molecules to the air.

Electrochemical Series   (See *Electromotive Series*.)

Electrode   The points at which a current leaves and enters an electrolyte during electrolysis. (See also *Anode, Cathode, Electrolysis*.)

Electrolysis   The decomposition of compounds by electricity. For example, we can decompose water into hydrogen and oxygen by running an electric current through a very weak solution of water and sulfuric acid. The positively charged hydrogen ions collect at the cathode, gain electrons, and so become neutral hydrogen atoms. Two such atoms (H + H) join as a hydrogen molecule (H_2) and escape as a gas. The negatively charged oxygen ions collect at the anode, where they lose electrons, and so become neutral oxygen atoms. Two such atoms (O + O) join as an oxygen molecule (O_2) and escape as a gas. This continues until there is no water left. Very active elements can be obtained only by this method.

Electrolyte   A compound which conducts a current when in a water solution. For example, sulfuric acid is the electrolyte in the electrolysis of water. (See *Electrolysis*.)

Electromotive Series   A list of metals in order of their decreasing tendency to lose electrons and become ions. The metals near the top lose electrons most easily, those near the bottom less easily.

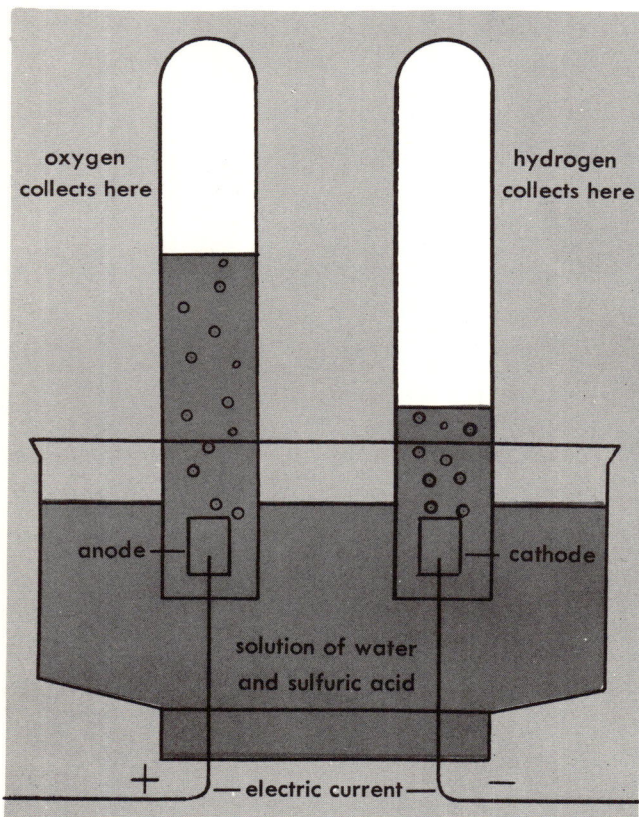

oxygen collects here

hydrogen collects here

anode

cathode

solution of water and sulfuric acid

+ — electric current — −

ELECTROMOTIVE SERIES
Potassium
Sodium
Calcium
Magnesium
Aluminum
Zinc
Iron
Hydrogen
Copper
Mercury
Silver
Platinum
Gold

Electron   A negative unit of electricity. Clouds of electrons surround the nuclei of atoms. The mass of an electron is $\frac{1}{1840}$ that of the hydrogen atom.

ATOMS WITH 1 SHELL

hydrogen
1 electron

helium
2 electrons

THE ARRANGEMENT
OF ELECTRONS
IN THE SHELLS OF ATOMS

ATOMS WITH 2 SHELLS

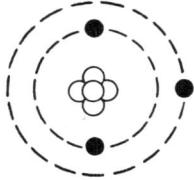

lithium
3 electrons

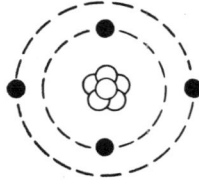

beryllium
4 electrons

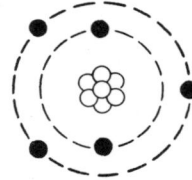

boron
5 electrons

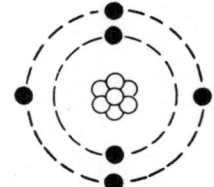

carbon
6 electrons

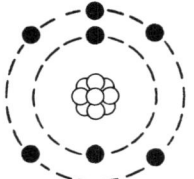

nitrogen
7 electrons

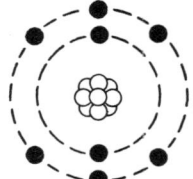

oxygen
8 electrons

fluorine
9 electrons

neon (inert gas)
10 electrons

ATOMS WITH 3 SHELLS

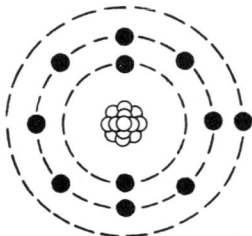

sodium
11 electrons

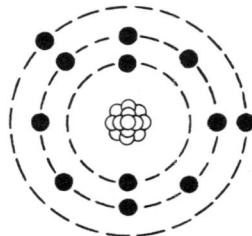

magnesium
12 electrons

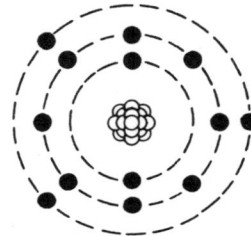

aluminum
13 electrons

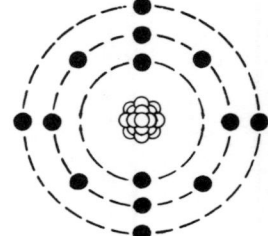

silicon
14 electrons

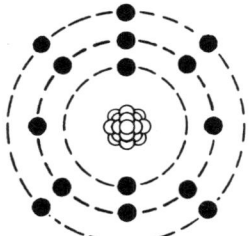

potassium
15 electrons

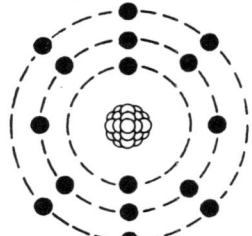

sulfur
16 electrons

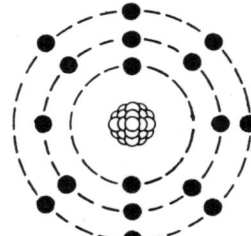

chlorine
17 electrons

argon (inert gas)
18 electrons

Electronegative Element An element that forms negative ions; for example, chlorine, oxygen, and sulfur.

Electron Microscope Unlike regular microscopes, which rely on ordinary light to illuminate an object, electron microscopes use a beam of electrons. Because the electrons have a greater resolving power than light (that is, they can better show up the differences between much smaller particles than ordinary light can), they reveal the structure of very small objects. Electron microscopes can magnify objects to about 100,000 times. (See photo, p. 32.)

Electron Shells The electrons of an atom re-

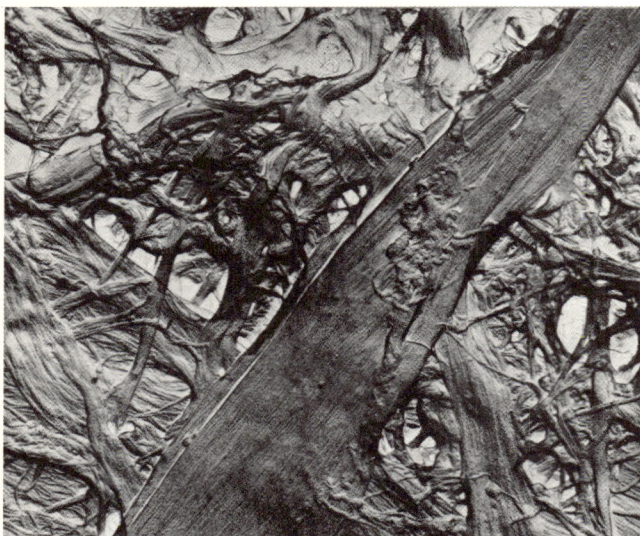

Cotton fibers, as seen in an electron microscope.

volve in shells about the nucleus. Because the electrons revolve at the rate of several billion times a second, centrifugal force prevents them from being drawn into the nucleus. Each element has a definite number of electrons that can exist in each shell of its atom. Hydrogen is the only atom which has a single electron. Helium has 2 electrons (the maximum number for the first shell), and because its shell is "full," helium will not react with other atoms. Atoms with "full" outer shells are said to be "inert" (for example, the inert gases comprising Group O in the periodic table). The electron arrangement of the atoms from hydrogen through argon are given here.

Electroplating Depositing a film of metal on the surface of some other substance—from metals to plastics—by electrolysis. To silver-plate a coffeepot, for instance, the pot and a bar of pure silver are placed in a solution of potassium silver cyanide, which serves as the electrolyte. When the current is switched on, the pot collects a plate of silver. During the process, the pot serves as the cathode, and the silver bar serves as the anode. (See also *Electrolysis* and *Battery*.)

Electropositive Element An element that forms positive ions, for example, hydrogen and copper.

Electrovalent Bond (See *Chemical Bonds* and *Valence*.)

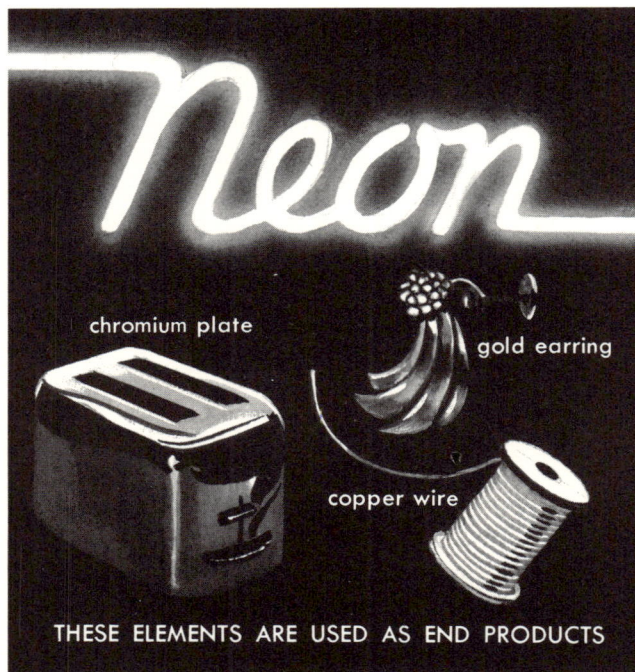

chromium plate

gold earring

copper wire

THESE ELEMENTS ARE USED AS END PRODUCTS

Element Any substance which cannot be broken down into a smaller unit by chemical means and which is composed entirely of the same kind of atoms. Gold, oxygen, and neon are elements. There are 103 known elements. Some elements that do not occur in nature can be made in the laboratory. (See special section on *Elements*, p. 68.)

Copper Plating

A film of copper can be deposited on a metal object in the following way: When a copper sheet (joined to the positive terminal) and the metal object to be coated (joined to the negative terminal) are bathed in a solution of copper sulfate, a thin coating of copper is gradually deposited on the metal object.

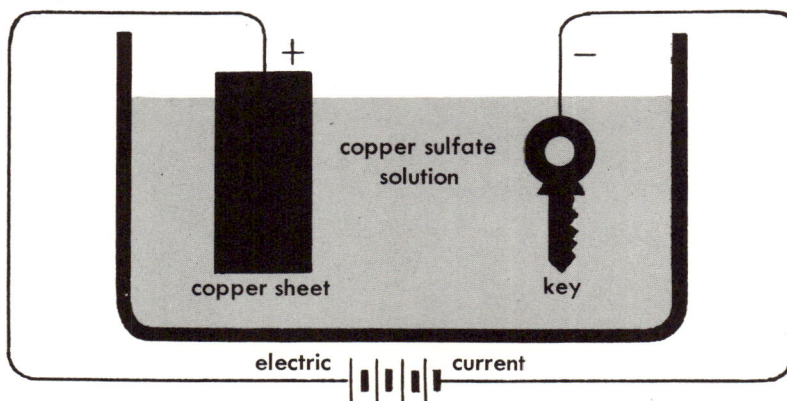

copper sulfate solution

copper sheet

key

electric current

Empirical Formula   (See *Formula*.)

Emulsion   One liquid dispersed evenly throughout another so that the two form a colloid. In photography, the term emulsion is misused when applied to the light-sensitive surface of the film. Actually this surface is a stabilized colloid.

Endothermic Reaction   A chemical reaction that takes place when the temperature is lowered. A reaction that absorbs energy (heat).

Enzymes   Chemical substances (catalysts) made by our body glands. They break down food physically and chemically so that it can go into solution and enter our body cells.

THE ACTION OF ENZYMES
(not a complete list)

NAME	GLAND	EFFECT
Ptyalin	Salivary	Changes starch into sugar
Pepsin	Gastric	Changes proteins to peptones
Rennin	Gastric	Curdles milk
Amylase (Diastase)	Pancreas	Changes starch to maltose
Lipase	Pancreas	Changes fats to glycerol and fatty acids
Trypsin	Pancreas	Changes proteins to amino acids
Erepsin	Glands in small intestine	Changes peptones to amino acids
Sucrase	Glands in small intestine	Changes sucrose to glucose
Maltase	Glands in small intestine	Changes maltose to glucose

Equation   A shorthand method of representing a chemical reaction, the letters and numerals representing the kinds and numbers of atoms taking part in the reaction. For example, when hydrogen and chlorine react, we represent the reaction by the following equation which shows that 2 atoms of hydrogen combine with 2 atoms of chlorine, and form 2 molecules of hydrogen chloride. $H_2 + Cl_2 \rightarrow 2HCl$. (See also *Formula*.)

Equilibrium   (See *Chemical Equilibrium*.)

Equivalent Weight   (See *Combining Weight*.)

Ester   An organic salt produced by the combination of an organic acid and an organic base (alcohol) by the removal of water. For example:

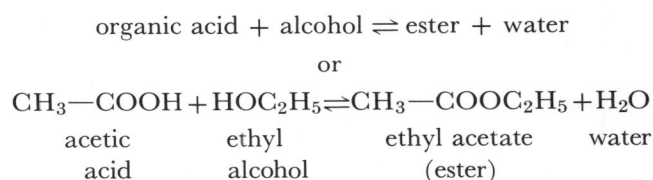

$$\text{organic acid} + \text{alcohol} \rightleftharpoons \text{ester} + \text{water}$$
$$\text{or}$$
$$CH_3{-}COOH + HOC_2H_5 \rightleftharpoons CH_3{-}COOC_2H_5 + H_2O$$

| acetic acid | ethyl alcohol | ethyl acetate (ester) | water |

Many esters are sweet-smelling liquids. Fruit and flower odors are produced by evaporating esters.

SOME COMMON ESTERS

NAME	FORMULA	ODOR
Amyl acetate	$CH_3COOC_5H_{11}$	Pear
Isoamyl acetate	$CH_3COOC_5H_{11}$	Banana
Octyl acetate	$CH_3COOC_8H_{17}$	Orange
Methyl butyrate	$C_3H_7COOCH_3$	Pineapple
Butyl butyrate	$C_3H_7COOC_4H_9$	Pineapple
Amyl valerate	$C_4H_9COOC_5H_{11}$	Apple

Sweet odors of a pineapple and rose are due to esters.

Etching   A process of producing a design on metal. If a wax-coated surface of metal is tooled

Designs and type for printing can be made if a metal surface is treated with wax, then bathed with an acid.

in such a way that a design is cut in the wax and the surface exposed along the lines of design, acid poured over the designed surface will attack the exposed metal but not the areas covered by wax. When the wax coating is finally removed, the etched surface can be used as a printing plate. Glass can also be etched.

Ethanol   Ethyl alcohol (see *Alcohol*).

Ether   Diethyl ether—$(C_2H_5)_2O$. A sweet-smelling liquid used as a solvent and anesthetic.

Evaporation   The process of changing a liquid to a vapor. The escape into the air of molecules forming the surface region of a liquid. Most of the molecules below the surface of a liquid are trapped by other molecules all around them, but those at or near the surface of the liquid are free to "take off" into the air. This is what happens when a pan of water evaporates.

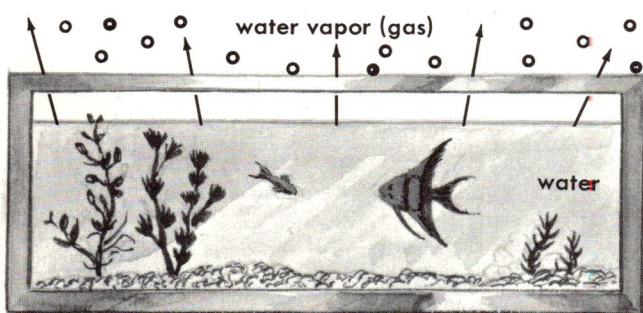

water vapor (gas)

water

Exothermic Reaction   A chemical reaction that takes place when the temperature is increased. A reaction that liberates energy (heat). About 95% of all chemical reactions are exothermic.

F

Fahrenheit Scale   The temperature scale on which water freezes at 32° and boils at 212° at standard atmospheric pressure (760 mm.). Nine Fahrenheit degrees equal 5 Centigrade degrees. To convert from Fahrenheit to Centigrade, subtract 32 from the Fahrenheit reading, multiply by 5, then divide by 9. (See also *Centigrade Scale*.)

Fallout   Small radioactive particles resulting from a nuclear explosion and falling on a large area. In high enough concentrations they contaminate everything they touch, damaging many of the cells of living matter.

Fats   Organic compounds composed of glyceryl esters of fatty acids such as stearic, palmitic, and oleic acids. Oils such as linseed oil and olive oil are the same as fats. (See *Ester*.)

Fermentation   The changing of sugar into alcohol and carbon dioxide by enzymes produced by yeast, bacteria, and other living organisms. In wine making, the juice of grapes is exposed to the air, and before long it begins to bubble. What happens is that the grape sugar (dextrose) is changed into alcohol and carbon dioxide bubbles by a yeast (enzyme).

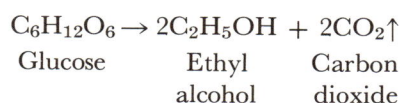

$$C_6H_{12}O_6 \rightarrow 2C_2H_5OH + 2CO_2\uparrow$$

Glucose   Ethyl   Carbon
                 alcohol   dioxide

Fertilizer   Any substance which adds to the soil compounds necessary for plant growth; e.g., nitrogen, phosphorus, and potassium. Because modern farming techniques remove nitrogen from the soil faster than nature can restore it, we need nitrogen fertilizers such as manures and fish scraps, and calcium cyanamide ($CaCN_2$), prepared in the laboratory. Wood ashes make a good fertilizer because they provide the soil with potash, or potassium carbonate (K_2CO_3). (See also *Nitrogen Cycle*.)

Filtrate   The clear liquid which has been separated from impurities during filtration.

Filtration   The separation of impurities from a liquid by passing the liquid through a filter of paper, cloth, or some other porous material.

Filtration of Water   The second step in the purification of water. The water is passed through a filter (sand or some other substance) to remove impurities. (See *Water Purification* diagram.)

Fire   (See *Combustion*.)

Firedamp   An explosive gas formed in coal mines when methane (CH_4) mixes with air.

Fission   The breaking or splitting of the nucleus of an atom into two pieces of about the same size, during which process radiation is emitted. The splitting of an atom by bombarding it with a slow neutron. When a uranium atom (U^{235}) is split, its two new parts become an atom of krypton and an atom of barium. (See also *Chain Reaction*.)

Fixation of Nitrogen   (See *Nitrogen Cycle*.)

Fixing   In photography, the process of soaking the developed film in hypo (sodium thiosulphate—$Na_2S_2O_3 \cdot 5H_2O$) so that the film will no longer be sensitive to light. This is achieved as the hypo changes the silver halides (AgCl or AgBr) into a soluble compound. (See also *Developer*.)

Flame   The visible effect of burning, in the form of a glowing gas. In a Bunsen burner, white-hot particles of free carbon make the flame visible.

Flame Test   A test to identify metals in a compound. Dip the end of a platinum wire in the compound you want to test, then hold the wire in flame. The following colors (top of next column) will enable you to identify the metal in the compound.

FLAME TEST COLORS	
METAL	COLOR
Barium	Yellow-green
Calcium	Orange-red
Copper	Blue-green
Lithium	Red
Potassium	Violet
Sodium	Yellow
Strontium	Red

Fluorescence   The ability of many substances to absorb ultraviolet (invisible) light and emit visible light. Fluorescent substances cease to shine when their source of ultraviolet light is cut off. Fluorescent lighting tubes contain mercury which becomes vaporized when an electric charge runs through the tube. The vaporized mercury gives off ultraviolet rays which cause the material coating the inside of the tube to emit visible light. Phosphorescent substances, unlike fluorescent substances, continue to glow for a time after the energy source (ultraviolet rays or X rays) has been cut off.

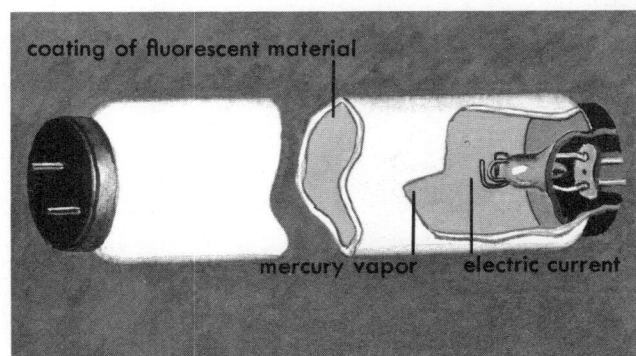

coating of fluorescent material

mercury vapor   electric current

Fluoridation   (of drinking water): Adding small amounts of sodium fluoride to drinking water in order to reduce the rate of tooth decay as the water is consumed. The protective coating of our teeth contains calcium fluoride and calcium silicate. It has been proved that drinking water containing appreciable amounts of fluorine compounds is beneficial in checking tooth decay.

Flux Any substance that helps remove the worthless ore material during the smelting of metals. Limestone is the flux used during the smelting of iron ore. A flux is also the product used to clean the surfaces of metals to be welded or soldered. Borax is a common flux.

Formaldehyde A gas—HCHO. Produced by the oxidation of methanol. Used widely in the manufacture of plastics.

Formalin A 40% solution of formaldehyde. Used as a preservative of biological specimens and as a disinfectant.

Formula 1. **Molecular Formula**—a shorthand system of representing *the number of atoms* that make up a molecule. For example, H_2O is the molecular formula for water; H_2 stands for two atoms of hydrogen, and O stands for one atom of oxygen. 2. **Structural Formula**—using the alphabetic letters of a formula to represent in "picture" form the molecule; for example, water would be H—O—H. These formulas show the number *and arrangement* of atoms in a compound. 3. **Empirical Formula**—the simplest formula, which shows *only the ratio of atoms* making up a molecule, while the molecular formula shows the actual number. Example of an empirical formula is CH_2O; it tells you only that there are twice as many hydrogen atoms as there are carbon or oxygen atoms, so the molecular formula could be $C_2H_4O_2$, or $C_6H_{12}O_6$, and so on.

Fraction A name given to the products which boil between certain temperature ranges in the fractional distillation of crude oil. Petroleum fractions are gasoline, kerosene, fuel oil, petrolatum, asphalt, and so on. (See *Fractionating Tower* and illustration below.)

Fractionating Tower Crude oil taken from the ground is heated to its boiling point, then the vapors are piped into a fractionating (or bubble) tower. The tower is hottest at the bottom and becomes cooler toward the top. Arranged from the bottom to the top of the tower are a series of condensation units which collect and separate the crude-oil vapors according to their condensation temperature. The condensation order of end products (called "fractions") is shown here, together with a diagram showing what happens to the crude oil from the time it is taken from the ground. Before the end products can be used, they must be purified.

Crude oil is heated in such a way that different products are boiled off at different temperatures.

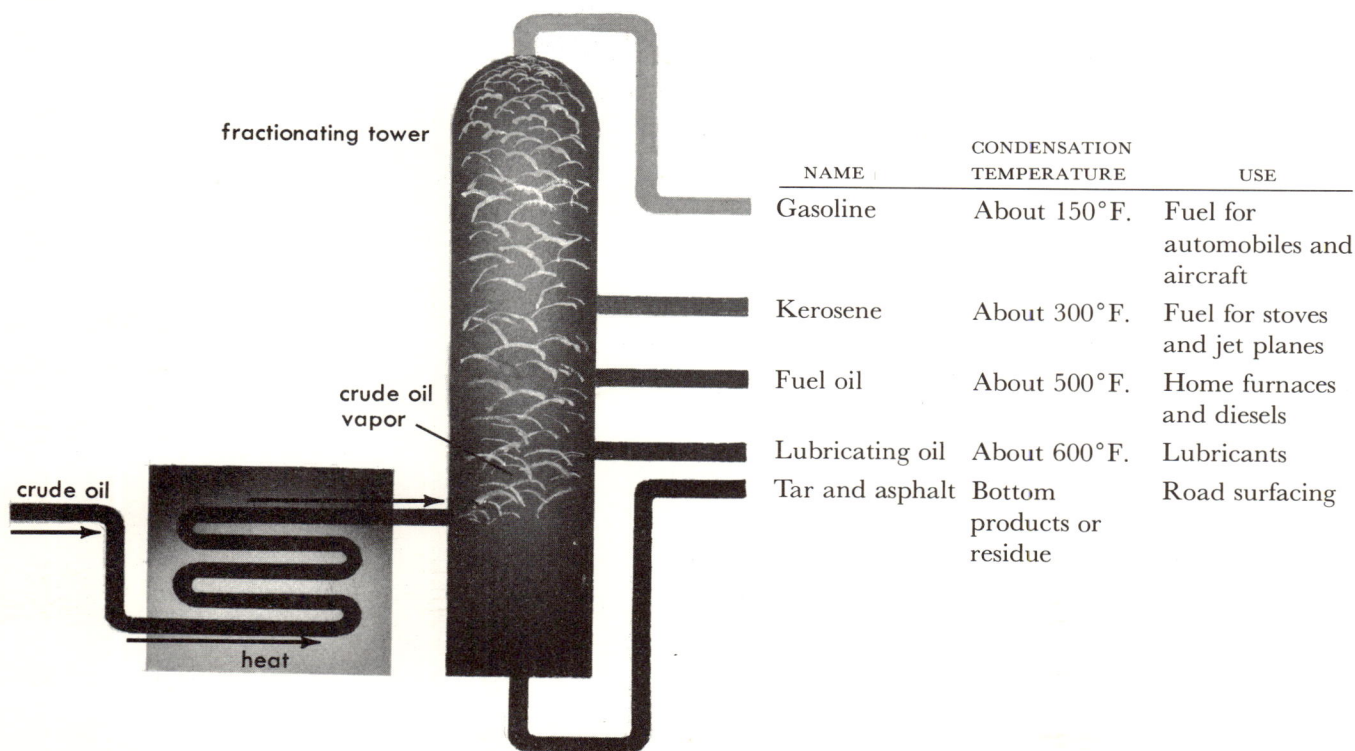

NAME	CONDENSATION TEMPERATURE	USE
Gasoline	About 150°F.	Fuel for automobiles and aircraft
Kerosene	About 300°F.	Fuel for stoves and jet planes
Fuel oil	About 500°F.	Home furnaces and diesels
Lubricating oil	About 600°F.	Lubricants
Tar and asphalt	Bottom products or residue	Road surfacing

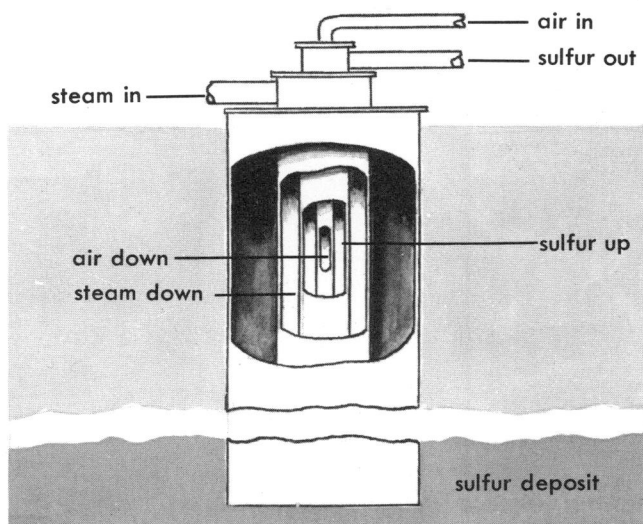

Frasch Process A method of mining sulfur deposits deep underground. First, concentric pipes (pipes within pipes) are sunk to the level of the sulfur deposit. Next, superheated steam or hot water under pressure is pumped down to melt the sulfur, then air is forced down. The pressure of the air forces the melted sulfur to flow up to the surface.

Freezing The changing of a substance from a liquid to a solid. In a frozen state, the molecules of a substance are rather firmly fixed in a crystal pattern. Instead of moving about, as they do in a liquid state, they remain fixed and vibrate.

Freezing Point The temperature at which a liquid becomes a solid.

Fuel Oil A mixture of several different hydrocarbon molecules, one of which is $C_{16}H_{34}$. Like kerosene, fuel oil is difficult to vaporize and burn, so it is not well suited to internal combustion engines. Home oil-burner furnaces spray fuel oil through a nozzle; on mixing with air it burns easily. Fuel oil, like kerosene, can be used in diesel engines. (See *Fractionating Tower*.)

Fusion The bringing together of substances, as opposed to fission, which means splitting apart. An enormous amount of heat (about 20 million degrees C.) causes the nuclei of light atoms to fuse. For example, inside the sun, hydrogen atoms fuse and form helium. When the nuclei of heavy hydrogen (tritium and deuterium) combine, tremendous energy is released. The result on a large scale is the hydrogen bomb. So much heat is required to trigger the fusion of deuterium and tritium nuclei, that no laboratory methods to date can do the job. But the enormous heat liberated when an atomic (fission) bomb explodes is enough to bring about fusion. A hydrogen bomb, then, is simply a fission bomb surrounded by heavy water. The heat resulting from fission triggers the fusion of deuterium and tritium atoms making up the heavy water. Fusion releases more energy than fission.

Fusion, heat of (See *Heat*.)

G

Galvanize To coat with zinc. Because zinc resists corrosion, it is used to protect the surface of other metals. Hardware items of various kinds (nails and roofing metal) are dipped in molten zinc. This process of coating is called *galvanization*.

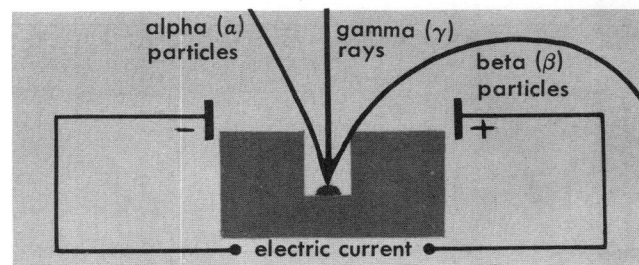

Gamma Rays Written γ rays. Extremely penetrating, (therefore dangerous) high-speed waves which have a shorter wave length than visible light. When a gamma ray is created, matter is converted into energy. Gamma rays usually accompany the escape of alpha and beta particles.

FUSION OF DEUTERIUM AND TRITIUM

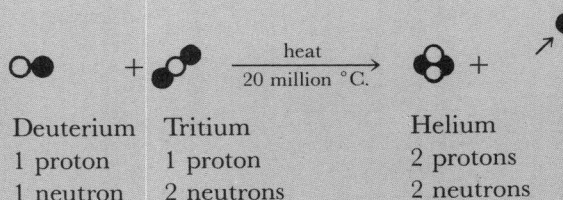

Deuterium	Tritium	Helium
1 proton	1 proton	2 protons
1 neutron	2 neutrons	2 neutrons

water as liquid

water as gas (steam)

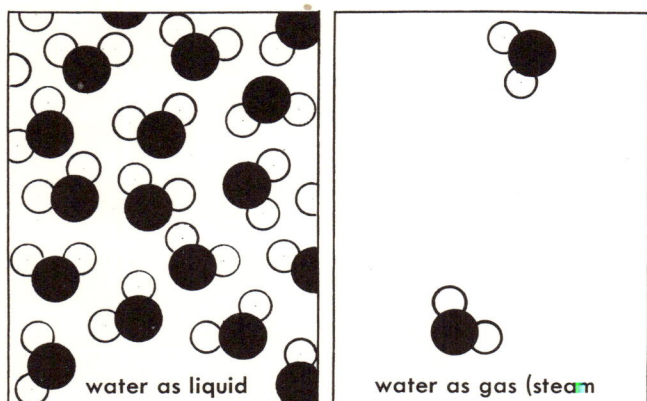

Gaseous State A loose collection of molecules which has no particular form or shape. The molecules making up a gas distribute themselves evenly throughout the area that contains them. If the gas is not compressed, the distance between molecules is very great compared with the dimensions of the molecules. (See also *Liquid State, Solid State*.)

Gasoline A volatile mixture of several hydrocarbons with a low boiling point. Gasoline includes molecules of hexane (C_6H_{14}), heptane (C_7H_{16}), and octane (C_8H_{18}). Because it is volatile, it is well suited for use in internal combustion engines. When gasoline is ignited in an engine, it produces carbon dioxide, water vapor, and heat:

$$2C_6H_{14} + 19O_2 \rightarrow 12CO_2 + 14H_2O + heat$$

Gay-Lussac's Law (See special section on *Chemical Laws*, p. 73.)

Gel Colloidal particles which have been coagulated by a change in temperature of the solution.

Glass Window and bottle glass are made from a simple mixture of sand (SiO_2), limestone ($CaCO_3$), and soda ash (Na_2CO_3). When the three are heated above 1260°C., the materials fuse and carbon dioxide is liberated. Glass, then, is composed of sodium silicate, calcium silicate, and silica (sand). On heating, the following reactions take place:

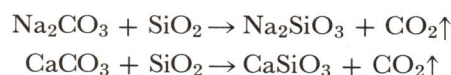

$$Na_2CO_3 + SiO_2 \rightarrow Na_2SiO_3 + CO_2\uparrow$$
$$CaCO_3 + SiO_2 \rightarrow CaSiO_3 + CO_2\uparrow$$

1. Window Glass—A ribbon of glass from the furnace is drawn out, cooled, and cut to length. **2. Plate Glass**—Molten glass is poured into a flat mold, cooled, then ground and polished on both sides. Plate glass is also made in a continuous process. **3. Optical Glass**—A combination of crown glass (a lime-soda glass) and flint (a lead and potassium-silicates glass), which is clear, bright, and free of color-fringe error (called chromatic aberration). **4. Low-Expansion Glass**—(see *Pyrex*). **5. Safety Glass**—Two sheets of glass bonded on either side of a film of plastic. When the glass is broken, it sticks to the plastic sheet instead of shattering. **6. Tempered Glass**—A sheet of glass with a flexible middle layer which allows bending without breaking.

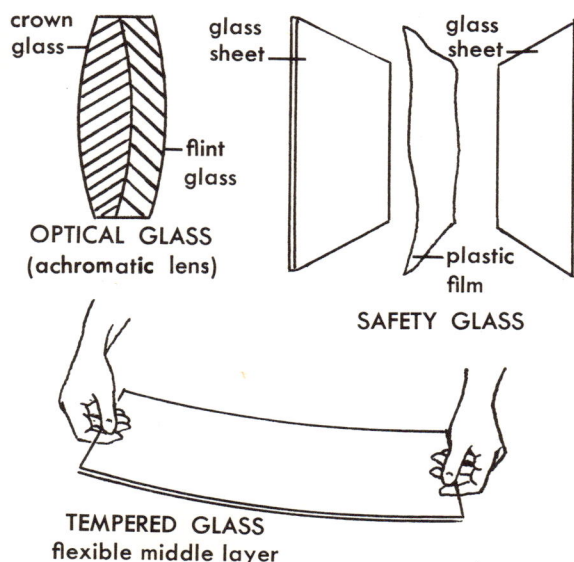

Different kinds of glass are determined by how they are processed and what is put into them. Fine glassmaking, represented by the vase shown in the photograph here, is an art as well as a craft.

COURTESY STEUBEN GLASS

crown glass — flint glass

OPTICAL GLASS (achromatic lens)

glass sheet — glass sheet — plastic film

SAFETY GLASS

TEMPERED GLASS flexible middle layer

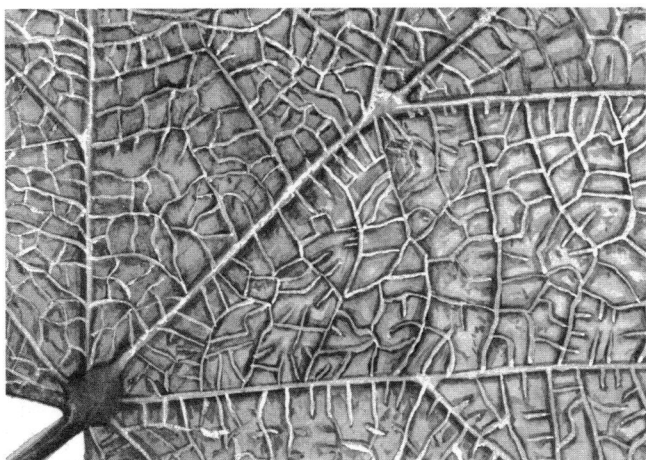

Glucose, a sugar, is formed and stored in the fine tissues of all green plants during photosynthesis.

Glucose   Grape sugar—$C_6H_{12}O_6$. Also called *dextrose*. Enzymes in our bodies convert other sugars and carbohydrates into glucose ("blood sugar") so that this important fuel can be converted into energy.

Glycerin   Glycerol—$C_3H_5(OH)_3$. Used in making explosives (see *Nitroglycerin*) and cellophane. A by-product of soap (see *Soap*).

Gram   (g.) A unit for measuring mass. One gram equals $\frac{1}{1000}$ kilogram (0.0022 pound).

Gram-atomic Weight   The weight of an atom of an element expressed in grams. The gram-atomic weight of oxygen is 16; of iron 55.5.

Gram-molecular Volume   The volume that has 1 gram-molecule (or mole) of a gas at standard conditions. The gram-molecular volume of a gas is 22.4 liters.

Gram-molecular Weight   (Mole) The weight of a molecule of an element or a compound expressed in grams. The gram-molecular weight of water is 18 g. (1 atom of oxygen = 16; and 2 atoms of hydrogen = 2).

Grape Sugar   Glucose—$C_6H_{12}O_6$.

Graphite   An allotropic form of carbon found in nature; also called *plumbago*. Made of crystals in the shape of thin, flat plates which slide over one another easily; hence its use as a lubricant. Graphite is made by running a strong electrical charge through hard coal. The chief difference between diamond and graphite is their arrangement of carbon atoms. In graphite, the atoms are attached to each other in such a way that they form giant flat molecules only one atom thick. These molecules are held together in layers by weak forces which are easily broken, allowing the layers to slip over one another when pressure is applied. (See *Allotropy*.)

Gypsum   Hydrated calcium sulfate crystals formed by warming sea water—$CaSO_4 \cdot 2H_2O$. When heated to 120°C. the compound loses most of its water of crystallization and becomes plaster of Paris.

H

Half-life   The length of time it takes a given sample of a radioactive element to lose one-half of its radioactivity. For example, one-half of any amount of radium takes 1620 years to "decay." Half of the remaining amount (one-quarter the amount of the original) will also take 1620 years to decay, and so on.

HALF-LIFE OF RADIOACTIVE ELEMENTS		
ISOTOPE OF ELEMENT	SYMBOL	HALF-LIFE
Uranium	$_{92}U^{238}$	4.498×10^9 years
Uranium	$_{92}U^{234}$	2.67×10^5 years
Thorium	$_{90}Th^{234}$	24.1 days
Thorium	$_{90}Th^{230}$	8.0×10^4 years
Protactinium	$_{91}Pa^{234}$	1.14 minutes
Radium	$_{88}Ra^{226}$	1620 years
Lead	$_{82}Pb^{214}$	26.8 minutes
Lead	$_{82}Pb^{210}$	22 years

Halides   The simplest salts of the halogens; for example, hydrogen fluoride (H_2F_2) and hydrogen iodide (HI).

Halogens   The family name (meaning "salt producer") given to the five elements fluorine, chlorine, bromine, iodine, and astatine. Each of the halogens has seven electrons in its outer shell, so each combines readily with an atom offering an electron to make a complete shell of eight electrons.

Hardness   A substance can be hard only in relation to some other substance. If one substance (diamond, say) is able to scratch another substance (glass), then diamond is proved to be harder than glass. See the accompanying table of hardness values.

Hard Water   Water that contains calcium, magnesium, and iron compounds in solution. When hard water is used for washing, and soap is added to it, the soap enters into a chemical reaction with the dissolved minerals and produces an insoluble soap or scum. The scum consists of salts of the minerals and fatty acids of the soap.   **1. Temporary Hard Water**—contains bicarbonates of metals; for example, calcium hydrogen carbonate, $Ca(HCO_3)_2$. Boiling softens this water by decomposing the compound as follows:

$$Ca(HCO_3)_2 \rightarrow CaCO_3\downarrow + H_2O + CO_2\uparrow$$

HARDNESS OF MINERALS

One way we can identify minerals is to test their hardness. We measure the hardness by determining the mineral's resistance to abrasion or scratching. Mohs' scale, which follows, ranges from 1–10 and involves common articles and typical minerals as standards. With a little practice you should be able to test the hardness of substances fairly accurately. When you scratch one substance with another, the scratch should be a groove, not just a chalklike mark.

Talc	Easily scratched by the fingernail
Gypsum	Scratched with difficulty by fingernail; will not scratch a copper coin
Fingernail	Will scratch gypsum; will not scratch calcite. Hardness about 2.5
Calcite	Scratches copper and is scratched by copper; not scratched by fingernail
Copper	Scratches calcite; will not scratch fluorite. Hardness about 3
Fluorite	Scratches copper; will not scratch apatite or glass
Apatite	Scratches glass with difficulty and is scratched by glass with difficulty
Glass	Scratches apatite; will not scratch feldspar. Hardness 5.5–6
Feldspar (Orthoclase)	Scratches glass easily; scratched with difficulty by a knife blade
Knife blade	Scratches feldspar; will not scratch quartz. Hardness about 7
Quartz	Not scratched by knife blade; scratched with difficulty by a file
File	Scratches quartz with difficulty; will not scratch topaz. Hardness about 7
Topaz	Scratches quartz; will not scratch corundum
Corundum	Scratches topaz with difficulty; will scratch and is scratched by silicon carbide
Silicon carbide (Carborundum)	Scratches corundum; will not scratch diamond. Hardness about 9
Diamond	Will scratch any other substance; is not scratched by any known substance

COURTESY THE PERMUTIT COMPANY

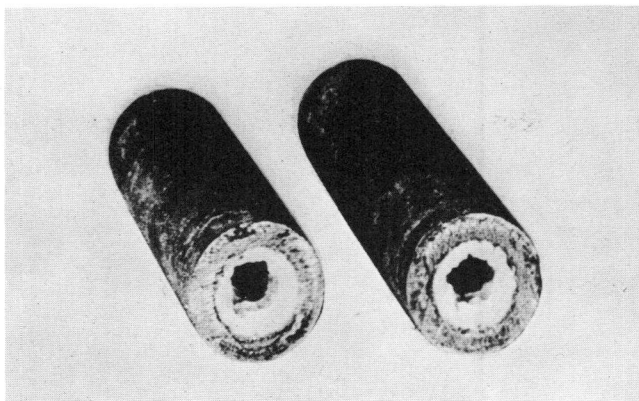

Hard water scale formed on the inside of these pipes.

The calcium carbonate settles out as a precipitate, and the carbon dioxide bubbles off as a gas, leaving H_2O. **2. Permanent Hard Water**—contains sulfates or chlorides of metals; for example, calcium chloride, $CaCl_2$. To soften this water we must add a compound such as soda ash (Na_2CO_3) whose sodium ions will replace the calcium ions in the calcium chloride. When the reaction takes place, calcium carbonate settles out as a precipitate as follows:

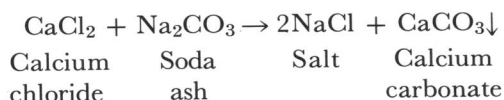

$$CaCl_2 + Na_2CO_3 \rightarrow 2NaCl + CaCO_3\downarrow$$

| Calcium chloride | Soda ash | Salt | Calcium carbonate |

Borax, $Na_2B_4O_7 \cdot 10H_2O$ (which yields sodium ions), or trisodium phosphate, Na_3PO_4, can also be used.

Heat A form of energy produced by the motions of molecules; measured in calories or in degrees of temperature. Although two substances are the same temperature, one may contain *more heat* than the other. For example, a bucket of water 100°C. contains a greater amount of heat than a cup of water 100°C. You can melt more ice with the *amount* of heat in the bucket than you can with the *amount* in the cup. Heat depends on the weight of the substance, its temperature, and also on the kind of material making up the substance. **1. Heat of Formation**—the heat produced when two or more elements react to form a compound. **2. Heat of Fusion**—the amount of heat required to convert 1 g. of a solid to 1 g. of a liquid without increasing the temperature. **3. Specific Heat**—the amount of heat required to raise the temperature of 1 g. of a substance 1°C. **4. Heat of Vaporization**—the amount of heat required to convert 1 g. of a liquid to 1 g. of a gas without increasing the temperature. (See also *Latent Heat*.)

Heavy Hydrogen (See *Deuterium*.)

Heavy Water Deuterium oxide—D_2O. On combining with oxygen, deuterium forms heavy water. In 5000 parts of ordinary water is one part of heavy water. It can be separated from ordinary water by electrolysis. During the process the ordinary water decomposes much faster than the heavy water. As a result, the heavy water becomes more and more concentrated. Heavy water can be used as a moderator in uranium reactors. (See also *Moderator*.)

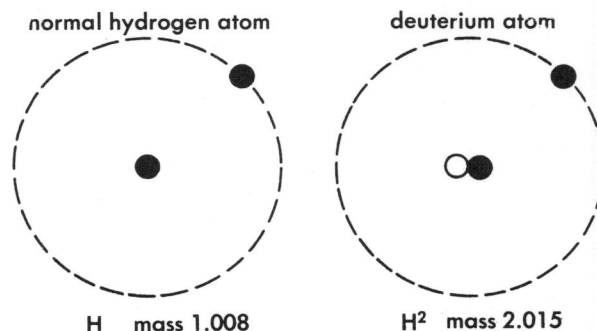

normal hydrogen atom   deuterium atom

H   mass 1.008 H^2 mass 2.015

The hydrogen atoms in heavy water (D_2O) are twice as massive as the hydrogen atoms in normal water.

Hematite Fe_2O_3. A rich source of iron, similar to rust in composition. It is the red coloring seen in bricks, red barn paint, and in some cosmetics.

Hemoglobin The red (iron-containing) part of the blood. Hemoglobin combines loosely with oxygen in the lungs, then carries the oxygen to the body tissues, where it is transferred to the cells.

Henry's Law (See special section on *Chemical Laws*, p. 73.)

Homogeneous Having a uniform composition throughout.

41

Homologous Series A group of compounds which are alike chemically and show a gradation in physical properties. For example, in the methane series each compound from methane to decane consists entirely of carbon and hydrogen atoms; but each succeeding compound in the series has a larger molecule, based on having one more atom of carbon and two more hydrogen atoms than the preceding compound in the series. The "general formula" for this series then is: C_nH_{2n+2}. (The general formula for the ethylene series is C_nH_{2n}.)

THE METHANE SERIES	
COMPOUND	FORMULA
Methane	CH_4
Ethane	C_2H_6
Propane	C_3H_8
Butane	C_4H_{10}
Pentane	C_5H_{12}
Hexane	C_6H_{14}
Heptane	C_7H_{16}
Octane	C_8H_{18}
Nonane	C_9H_{20}
Decane	$C_{10}H_{22}$

Hormones Complex organic compounds which serve as body-chemical regulators. They are produced by ductless glands, are carried by the blood to specialized organs of the body, and act as catalysts.

Hydrate A compound which combines with a definite proportion of water of crystallization; for example, when 1 molecule of copper sulfate ($CuSO_4$) combines with 5 molecules of water, we get copper sulfate pentahydrate ($CuSO_4 \cdot 5H_2O$). (See *Blue Vitriol*.)

Hydrocarbons Compounds made up of carbon and hydrogen only. Methane (CH_4) is the simplest hydrocarbon. For one series of hydrocarbons, see the *Methane Series*, left.

Hydrogenation Subjecting a substance to the chemical action of hydrogen. A process in which unsaturated oils or fats (such as cottonseed and linseed oils) are made into solid fats. Hard, edible fats such as oleomargarine, Crisco, and Spry are made this way. When cottonseed oil is treated with hydrogen, in the presence of a nickel catalyst, a hard, edible fat is produced.

Hydrogen Bomb (See *Fusion*.)

Hydrogen Peroxide H_2O_2. A syrupy liquid; dilute solutions are used as a disinfectant and bleaching agent.

Hydrogen Sulfide H_2S. A poisonous, colorless gas with the odor of rotten eggs. Its odor may be detected in some mineral waters containing sulfur. It is produced when organic material containing sulfur decays.

THE ACTION OF HORMONES

NAME	GLAND	EFFECT	NAME	GLAND	EFFECT
Pituitrin	Pituitary	Stimulates growth of the body's long bones; and stimulates the hormone production	Adrenalin	Adrenals	Prepares the body for emergencies; increases blood pressure; causes the liver to release sugar
Thyroxin	Thyroid	Regulates metabolism; supplies iodine, which is needed for good health	Insulin	Isles of Langerhans	Regulates sugar metabolism
			Parathormone	Parathyroids	Regulates calcium and phosphorus metabolism

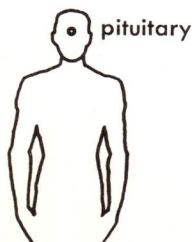

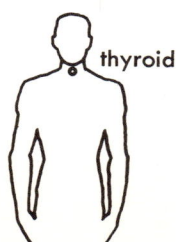

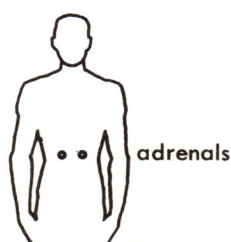

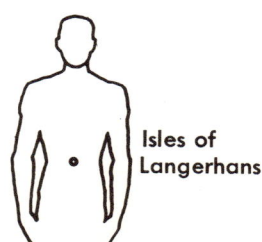

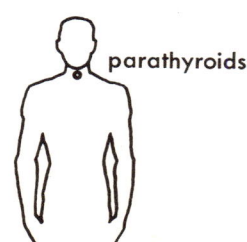

Hydrolysis 1. The combining of water and some other chemical during which process both are decomposed. The general equation:

$$XY + H_2O \rightleftharpoons X(OH) + HY$$

2. The reaction of water and a soluble salt to produce an excess of either H^+ (acid) ions or OH^- (base) ions. For example, "sour" (acid) soil can be "sweetened" by adding a phosphate fertilizer:

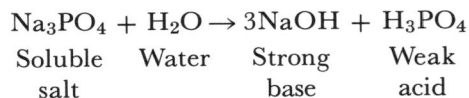

$$Na_3PO_4 + H_2O \rightarrow 3NaOH + H_3PO_4$$

Soluble salt	Water	Strong base	Weak acid

Hydrometer An instrument which measures the specific gravity of a liquid.

Hydroponics Growing plants in a solution of water and the minerals which plants normally extract from soil.

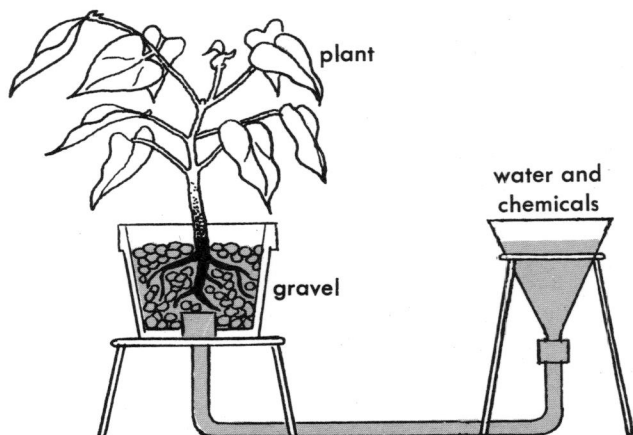

Diagram shows equipment for hydroponics experiment. Gravel is used to hold the roots in position.

Hydroxide Any compound that is prepared from water and that contains a $-OH$ radical. Hydroxides are prepared when one of the hydrogen atoms in the water molecule is replaced by some other atom, or group. For example,

$$2Na + 2H_2O \rightarrow 2NaOH + H_2$$

Hydroxyl A $-OH$ group. A radical consisting of 1 hydrogen atom and 1 oxygen atom. Alcohols, like bases, contain the $-OH$ group.

Hygroscopic The ability of any compound to absorb moisture. (See also *Deliquescent.*)

Hypo Sodium thiosulphate—$Na_2S_2O_3 \cdot 5H_2O$. (See *Fixing.*)

Hypothesis A general statement which attempts to explain certain observable facts which seem related. The statement *too much cigarette smoking can cause lung cancer* is a hypothesis. Experimentation can prove a hypothesis to be true or false. If enough proof supporting the hypothesis is collected, the hypothesis may become a law. (See entry *Law.*)

I

Igniting Temperature (See the entry *Kindling Temperature.*)

Inactivity The relative difficulty with which one element combines with another to form a compound. The inert gases, for example, will not combine with other elements.

Indicator A substance (litmus, for example) that reveals the nature of a solution by going through a sharp color change. The color change of litmus indicates whether the solution is acid or base. (See *Litmus.*)

Inert Inactive. The inert gases are helium, neon, argon, krypton, xenon, and radon. They will not combine with other elements. The outer shells of each of these atoms have all the electrons they can hold, so the atoms have no tendency to combine with other atoms, hence their chemical inactivity. (See also *Chemical Bonds, Electron Shells.*)

Inhibitor A substance that slows down or prevents a chemical reaction. A negative catalyst. A substance that prevents decomposition.

Inorganic Substances that do not contain carbon; for example, minerals.

Insoluble   A substance is said to be insoluble if it will not dissolve in some kind of liquid. (See also *Solubility*.)

Iodoform CHI_3. A yellow solid used as an antiseptic; prepared from acetone.

Ion Exchange   When ions forming a compound exchange partners. For example, when sodium ions replace calcium ions and calcium ions replace sodium ions in the following reaction:

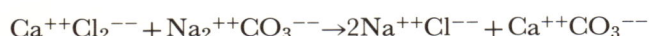

$$Ca^{++}Cl_2^{--} + Na_2^{++}CO_3^{--} \rightarrow 2Na^{++}Cl^{--} + Ca^{++}CO_3^{--}$$

(See also *Hard Water* and *Ions*.)

Ionization   The process of making ions. When an electrovalent compound such as salt—NaCl—is dissolved in water, the ions (Na^+Cl^-) of which the compound is composed are separated as individual particles. This solution is called an "electrolyte" because it conducts electricity.

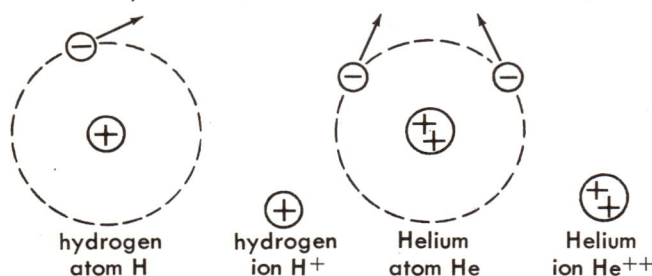

hydrogen atom H   hydrogen ion H^+ Helium atom He   Helium ion He^{++}

Ions   Electrically charged atoms or radicals. For example, atoms which, through either a loss or gain of electrons, have acquired either a positive or negative charge—negative ions or positive ions. Ions can be produced by creating an electric charge in a gas. When a hydrogen atom loses its single electron, the nucleus is left with its 1 proton, which carries a positive charge. The resulting ion is written H^+. When the helium atom, which has 2 protons in its nucleus, is deprived of its 2 electrons, the resulting ion is written He^{++}. (See also *Charge*.)

Isomers   Those compounds whose molecules are made up of the same kinds and numbers of atoms, but which have a different *arrangement* of atoms in the molecule. If there were "word isomers" the words NO and ON would do. Although they are made up of the same atoms (letters), their molecules (meanings) are different.

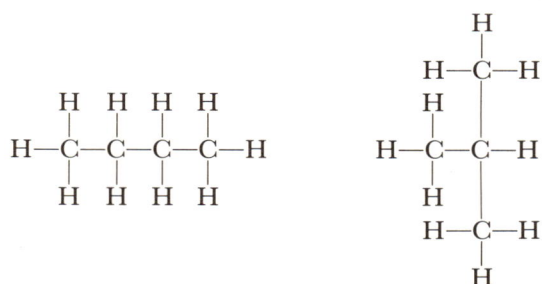

normal, or n-Butane C_4H_{10} Isobutane C_4H_{10}

Isotopes   Atoms of the same element that have different atomic weights, although they have the same atomic number. If an element has three isotopes, each isotope will have exactly the same arrangement of electrons, exactly the same number of protons, *but will have a different number of neutrons*—hence different atomic weights. The 90 elements occurring in nature have a total of more than 300 isotopes. While sodium has only one isotope, tin has 10.

SAMPLE ISOTOPES				
ELEMENT	ELEC-TRONS	NEU-TRONS	PRO-TONS	MASS NUMBER
HYDROGEN	1	0	1	1
deuterium	1	1	1	2
tritium	1	2	1	3
OXYGEN	8	8	8	16
isotope	8	9	8	17
isotope	8	10	8	18
CHLORINE	17	18	17	35
isotope	17	20	17	37

K

Kelvin Scale   (See *Absolute Scale*.)

Kerosene   A petroleum product used in heating units and engines, distilled from crude oil. (See *Fractionating Tower*.)

Ketones A group of organic compounds all having the group =C=O. For example, acetone—$(CH_3)_2CO$.

$$CH_3 \diagdown$$
$$C{=}O$$
$$CH_3 \diagup$$

Kiln An oven used for special purposes. Kilns may be lined with a variety of different substances to control the oven temperature. Limestone is converted to lime when it is cooked at 1000°C. in an oil flame in a limekiln.

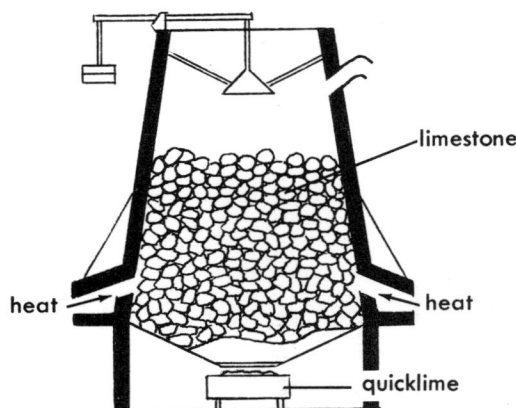

limestone

heat   heat

quicklime

Kilogram (kg.) 1000 grams, or 2.2 pounds.

Kilometer (km.) 1000 meters.

Kindling Temperature The temperature a substance must reach before it begins to burn. Different sorts of substances have different kindling temperatures.

Kinetic Molecular Theory The idea that all gases are composed of tiny particles called molecules and that they are in constant and rapid motion, bouncing off the walls of their container and colliding with one another. The higher the pressure of a gas, the more violently its molecules move about.

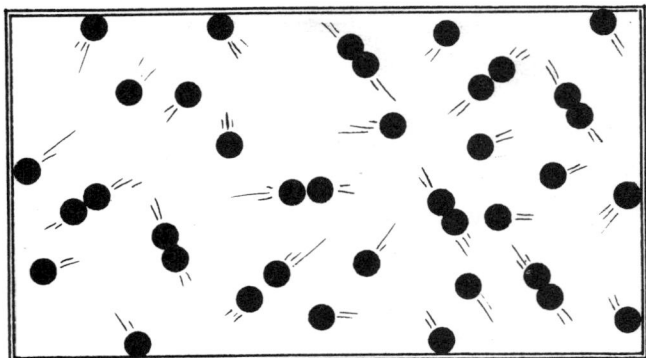

Knocking The effect produced when the mixture of gasoline vapor and air in the engine cylinder does not burn evenly. If the mixture burns too rapidly, or explodes, the gases within the cylinder expand faster than the piston can move back. Knocking wastes both fuel and power and places a strain on the engine. It can be caused by compressing the fuel-air mixture too much. In general, the higher the compression ratio of the engine, the higher octane rating of fuel you need. Knocking, then, can be caused by using a low-octane-rating fuel in a high-compression-ratio engine. (See also *Octane Number.*)

L

Lactose Milk sugar—$C_{12}H_{22}O_{11}$. The sweetening agent in milk. Lactose is an isomer of sucrose. Milk turns sour when its lactose changes into lactic acid. The change is brought about by bacteria. Pasteurizing the milk (heating it to 143°F. for 33 minutes) destroys most of the bacteria and so delays souring.

Latent Heat The amount of heat energy needed to change 1 g. of a substance from a solid to a liquid, or from a liquid to a gas without increasing the temperature. When we melt ice by putting it in a frying pan, we do not raise its temperature. The heat energy goes into changing the molecular arrangement from a crystal to a liquid form. As soon as all the ice is melted, however, then the temperature of the liquid begins to rise; therefore we no longer have latent heat. (See also *Heat.*)

Latex The chief source of rubber. It is a milky fluid obtained from rubber trees. When it is mixed with acetic acid ($CH_3 \cdot COOH$), it forms basic rubber, which is further treated. (See *Rubber.*)

Law A general statement which explains certain actions under given conditions. While a hypothesis is also a similar statement, a law can be regarded as a widely accepted hypothesis that has successfully withstood the test of time. One of the best-known laws in science is Newton's third law of motion: "For every action (or force) there is an equal and opposite reaction."

Law of Definite Proportions (See special section on *Chemical Laws,* p. 73.)

Law of Multiple Proportions (See special section on *Chemical Laws,* p. 73.)

Lignin The noncellulose part of wood often combined with cellulose. In the manufacture of pulp, the lignin must be removed to obtain pure cellulose. It is a sticky material that helps bind the cellulose fibers together.

Lignite Brown coal with a high percentage of hydrocarbons. It is thought to be an early-stage substance in the formation of bituminous coal.

Lime 1. **Quicklime**—calcium oxide, CaO. Made by heating limestone. 2. **Slaked Lime**—calcium hydroxide, $Ca(OH)_2$—used in wall plaster, bleaching powder, and paper. Made by combining quicklime with water:

$$CaO + H_2O \rightarrow Ca(OH)_2 + heat$$

3. **Soda Lime**—a solid produced by mixing sodium hydroxide (NaOH) with slaked lime $Ca(OH)_2$.

Lime-Soda Treatment The fourth stage in the purification of water. Lime and soda are added in the required amounts to make hard water soft. (See *Hard Water* and *Water Purification* diagram.)

Limestone Calcium carbonate—$CaCO_3$. It occurs in many caves.

Limewater Calcium hydroxide (slaked lime) —$Ca(OH)_2$—in a solution with water. If left exposed to the air, limewater turns milky. The cause of this is carbon dioxide (CO_2) of the air combining with the calcium and forming insoluble calcium carbonate in the following reaction:

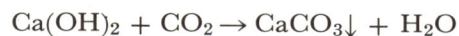

$$Ca(OH)_2 + CO_2 \rightarrow CaCO_3\downarrow + H_2O$$

Liquid Air Air which has been compressed and cooled until it has liquefied. It is largely a mixture of liquid oxygen and liquid nitrogen and has a temperature of $-200°C$. Since both oxygen and nitrogen have extremely low boiling points, they evaporate rapidly at room temperature. (Boiling point of oxygen is $-183°C$.; boiling point of nitrogen is $-196°C$.) Other gases can be liquefied.

Liquid State Any substance that is neither a gas nor a solid. Liquids have "shapes" only by taking on the shapes of their containers. The molecules of a liquid are less free to move about than molecules of a gas, but are more free to move about than molecules of a solid. Water and oil are examples of liquids. (See also *Gaseous State* and *Solid State.*)

Liter A measure of volume equal to the space occupied by 1000 g. of water at 4°C. and at standard pressure (760 mm.). Equal to 1000 c.c., or 1.06 qt.

Litmus A purple dye made from lichens (mosslike plants). Litmus is an indicator. Acids turn litmus paper red. Bases, on the other hand, turn it blue.

Lubricating Oil A product obtained by distilling crude oil. It is one of the higher boiling-point fractions. (See *Fractionating Tower.*)

Lye Caustic soda, a strong alkali. Sodium hydroxide—NaOH. Because lye is a very corrosive base, it is dangerous to handle.

M

Magnetite Fe_3O_4. Magnetic material making up about 5% of iron ore. It is 72% iron.

Malachite $Cu(OH)_2 \cdot CuCO_3$. A copper carbonate ore, greenish-blue in color. Also the green patina or verdigris on bronze statues and copper roofs.

Malleability   Any metal which can be hammered into thin sheets is said to be malleable. Gold is the most malleable of all metals.

Maltase   An enzyme found in yeast. It converts maltose into glucose. (See *Enzymes*.)

Maltose   Malt sugar—$C_{12}H_{22}O_{11}$. It is made when the enzyme diastase attacks starch.

Mass   The quantity of matter making up a body or a substance. (See also *Density*.)

Mass Number   The mass number of the nucleus of an atom is the sum of the number of neutrons and the number of protons. The mass number of hydrogen is 1, because it has only 1 proton making up its nucleus. The mass number of helium is 4, because it has 2 protons and 2 neutrons making up its nucleus. Uranium has a mass number of 238—the sum of its 92 protons and 146 neutrons.

Mass Spectrometer   An instrument used to determine the atomic weights of isotopes. Chlorine, for example, has 2 isotopes—one weighing 35 avograms, the other weighing 37 avograms. If chlorine gas is ionized, then a stream of ions containing both isotopes is deflected by a magnetic field and the 2 isotopes will be separated. The lighter ions will be bent more strongly by the magnetic field than the heavier ions. (See diagram.)

Matches   The heads of ordinary matches contain three substances: 1. a low-kindling material such as phosphorus sesquisulfide (P_4S_3); 2. potassium chlorate plus other oxidizing agents; 3. some material that burns easily, such as a mixture of potassium nitrate (KNO_3) and rosin. All of these materials are held together by glue and grit. The grit provides the necessary striking friction so that the match head will take fire when struck. Safety matches, which can be

The low kindling material on the striking surface of a box of safety matches begins to burn before the match.

struck only on a special surface, have the low-kindling material on the match box. If you strike a safety match in the dark you can see this for yourself, since the material on the box begins to burn first. Since the match head does not contain the low-kindling material, it cannot be struck on any material at hand.

Megaton   An explosive force equal to that of a million tons of TNT.

Melting Point   The temperature at which a solid changes to a liquid at standard pressure (760 mm.). The melting point for ice is 32°F. or 0°C.

Metabolism   The total chemical process that takes place in a living thing; the building up and breaking down of protoplasm; the conversion of food into energy.

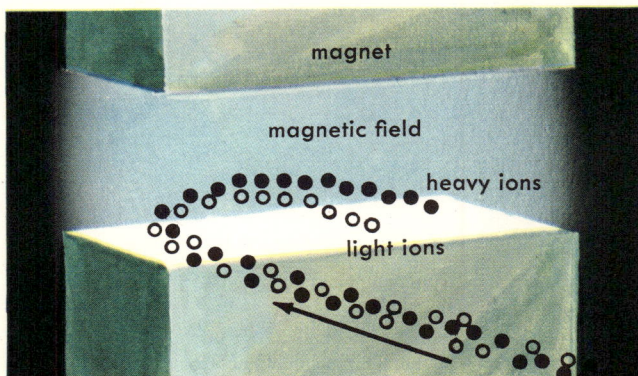

magnet

magnetic field

heavy ions

light ions

Metal Those elements which have certain things in common: they form positive ions, are opaque, are good conductors of electricity and heat, are hard and have a high density, and most have a silvery luster. Copper, gold, iron, and sodium are examples of the metals.

silver coins
90% silver
10% copper

cent
95% copper
3% tin
2% zinc

nickel coin
75% copper
25% nickel

Coins are made by blending several different kinds of metals in definite proportions.

Metallurgy The science of separating the metals from their ores and the study of the physical and chemical properties of metals.

Meter A unit for measuring length; originally intended to be 1/10,000,000 of a quadrant of the earth through Paris. Equal to 39.37 inches. (See *Metric System*.)

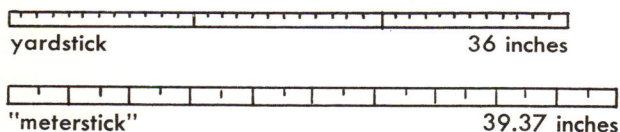

yardstick   36 inches

"meterstick"   39.37 inches

Methane Marsh gas; also firedamp—CH_4. It is formed by decaying organic material.

Methane Series (See *Homologous Series*.)

Methanol Methyl alcohol (see *Alcohol*).

Metric System A system of international measurement based on the meter, which is 39.37 inches. This standard length is preserved on a noncorroding bar of platinum-iridium kept in France, where the metric system was set up

just after the French Revolution. **1. Decimeter** —(dm.) 0.1 meter. **2. Centimeter**—(cm.) 0.01 meter. **3. Millimeter**—(mm.) 0.001 meter. **4. Kilometer**—(km.) 1000 meters.

Metric Ton 1000 kilograms, 2204.61 pounds.

Micron (μ) 0.001 mm.

Millimicron ($\mu\mu$) 0.000001 mm.

Minerals Rocks that have a characteristic chemical composition. For example, limestone, which is mostly calcium carbonate ($CaCO_3$); and sandstone, mostly silicon dioxide (SiO_2).

calcite
$CaCO_3$
specific gravity 2.72

gypsum
$CaSO_4 \cdot 2H_2O$
specific gravity 2.32

dolomite
$CaMg(CO_3)_2$
specific gravity 2.85

fluorite
CaF_2
specific gravity 3.18

halite
$NaCl$
specific gravity 2.16

Mixture A blend of substances in any proportion which do not combine chemically. For example, a mixture of iron filings and sand. The substances making up a mixture can be separated mechanically; the iron filings can be removed from the sand with a magnet. (See also *Compound*.)

Moderator A substance, such as graphite or heavy water, used in an atomic pile to absorb neutrons and so control the rate of fission.

Molar Solution A solution that has 1 gram-molecule (mole) of a compound contained in a 1-liter solution.

Mole The molecular weight of a substance in grams. (See *Gram-molecular Weight*.)

Molecular Weight The weight of a molecule of each element compared with a weight of 32 avograms assigned to an oxygen molecule. The molecular weight of a compound equals the sum of the weights of all atoms in the compound.

Molecule Two or more atoms chemically combined. The smallest piece of a substance above the size of an atom of that substance. The smallest quantity of water, for example, is a water molecule, consisting of 1 atom of oxygen and 2 atoms of hydrogen. One liter of oxygen contains 2.5×10^{22} molecules. With the electron microscope it is possible to see some of the giant organic molecules of viruses.

Monomer The small molecules which, when combined, become polymers. (See *Polymerization*.)

Mordant A fastening agent used in dyeing. For example, an aluminum hydroxide precipitate on cotton fibers acts as a substance for a dye to cling to, and so prevents it from being washed out when the cotton fabric is soaked in water. Basic mordants are used for acid dyes: and acid mordants are used for basic dyes.

N

Naphtha A gasolinelike solvent. Any mixture of hydrocarbons in various proportions. Wood naphtha is impure methyl alcohol.

Naphthalene $C_{10}H_8$, mothballs. Naphthalene occurs in coal tar. If naphthalene is chlorinated, it produces hydrochloric acid, as shown in the following reaction:

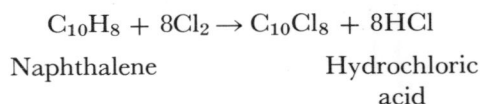

$$C_{10}H_8 + 8Cl_2 \rightarrow C_{10}Cl_8 + 8HCl$$

Naphthalene   Hydrochloric acid

Natural Gas Any gas or mixture of gases that are constantly being produced by the decay of vegetable matter. You can see bubbles of natural gas rise to the surface when you stir up the mud at the bottom of a pond. Great pockets of natural gas are usually found with oil deposits. The natural gas used in many kitchen stoves is largely methane—CH_4, which is produced by nature in swamps.

H_2O
water molecule

C_2H_6
ethane molecule

CH_4
methane (marsh gas) molecule

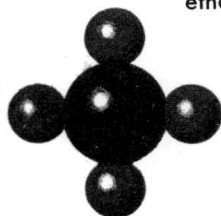

$C_6H_{12}O_6$
glucose molecule

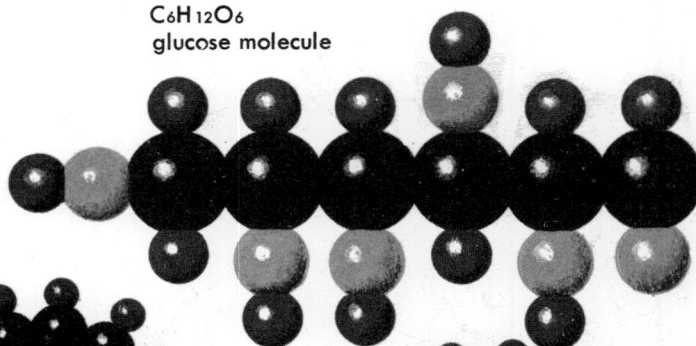

$C_{500}H_{1002}$
artificial rubber molecule

Neoprene A synthetic rubber made from vinyl acetylene; superior to natural rubber in many ways. (See table of *Synthetic Rubbers,* p. 79.)

Neutral 1. **Solution**—neither basic nor acid. 2. **Atom**—without an electric charge; all atoms which are not ions.

Neutralization Adding enough acid to a basic solution, or enough base to an acid solution so that the solution becomes neither acid nor basic; the result being a salt and water.

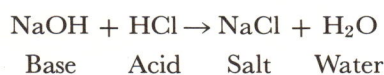

$$NaOH + HCl \rightarrow NaCl + H_2O$$

| Base | Acid | Salt | Water |

Neutron An electrically neutral particle in the nucleus of every atom except the hydrogen atom. Neutrons are slightly heavier than protons. Neutrons have great penetrating power because they are electrically neutral, but they have a short life outside the nucleus, lasting only 20 minutes before decomposing into an electron and a proton and giving off gamma rays.

Nitration The addition of —NO_2 (a nitro group) to an organic compound. (For example, nitrobenzene. See *Derivative.*)

Nitric Acid (See section on *Acids,* p. 83.)

Nitrogen Cycle The passage of nitrogen from the air and from animal waste into the soil, and from the soil into plants and then into animals. 1. **Nitrogen Fixation**—Free nitrogen from the air enters the soil, but is useless to plants in its free form. But when the nitrogen is combined in a compound (nitrates), the plants can use it. This combining ("fixing") is done by nitrogen-fixing bacteria which live attached to the roots of leguminous plants. 2. **Plant Food**—Thunderstorms are a source of nitrogen plant foods. A lightning flash combines free nitrogen in the air with oxygen, forming nitric oxide (2NO). The nitric oxide combines with more oxygen and forms nitrogen dioxide ($2NO_2$). The nitrogen dioxide is dissolved by rain and enters the soil as dilute nitric acid. Once in the soil, the nitric acid reacts with limestone (or some other substance) and is converted into calcium nitrate, one kind of plant food. The plant, which animals eat, locks this nitrogen in the form of a protein. The animals return the nitrogen to the soil in the form of waste matter. The following equations show how free nitrogen in the air is converted to calcium nitrate, a plant food:

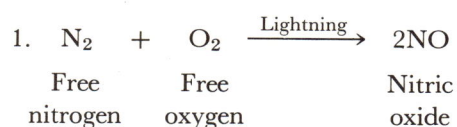

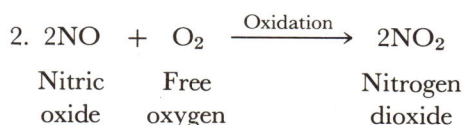

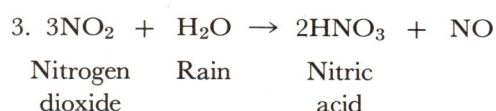

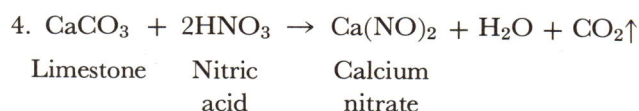

1. $N_2 + O_2 \xrightarrow{\text{Lightning}} 2NO$

| Free nitrogen | Free oxygen | Nitric oxide |

2. $2NO + O_2 \xrightarrow{\text{Oxidation}} 2NO_2$

| Nitric oxide | Free oxygen | Nitrogen dioxide |

3. $3NO_2 + H_2O \rightarrow 2HNO_3 + NO$

| Nitrogen dioxide | Rain | Nitric acid |

4. $CaCO_3 + 2HNO_3 \rightarrow Ca(NO)_2 + H_2O + CO_2\uparrow$

| Limestone | Nitric acid | Calcium nitrate |

Nitrogen gas, which makes up 78 per cent of the atmosphere, is exchanged between ground and air.

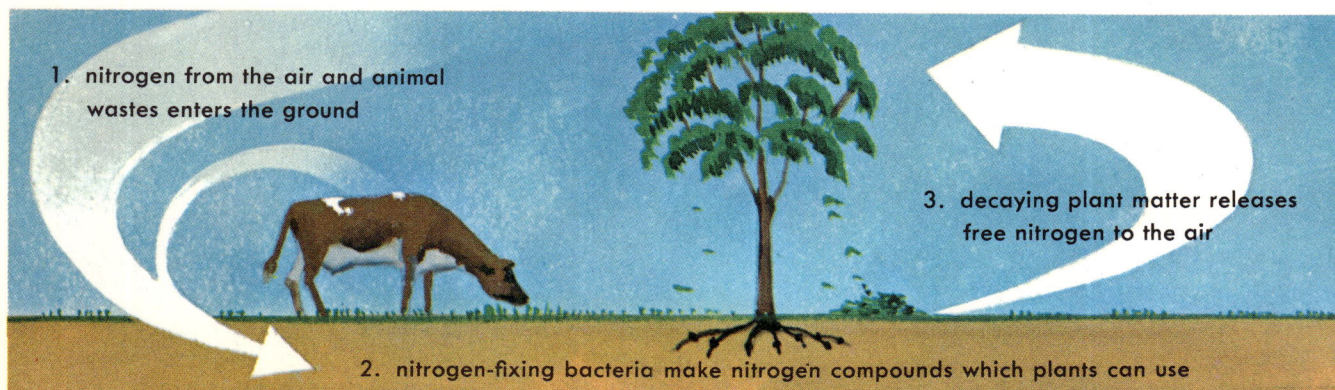

1. nitrogen from the air and animal wastes enters the ground

2. nitrogen-fixing bacteria make nitrogen compounds which plants can use

3. decaying plant matter releases free nitrogen to the air

Nitroglycerin Glyceryl trinitrate—$C_3H_5(NO_3)_3$. A violent explosive which can be set off by a sudden shock. Also used in medicine as a heart stimulant.

Noble Metals The metals that do not corrode easily or at all—gold, silver, platinum.

Nonpolar Bond A covalent bond that produces a molecule which is uniformly neutral. For example, the electrons shared by the 4 atoms of hydrogen and the single carbon atom making up methane (CH_4) are arranged in a symmetrical pattern, so there is no opportunity for the molecule to have a positive or a negative end. (See *Polar Bond* and *Chemical Bonds*.)

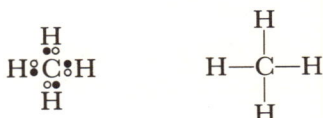

Normal Solution (N.) Any solution containing one gram-equivalent of a substance per liter; for example, 40 g. of sodium hydroxide ($NaOH$) dissolved in enough water to make 1 liter of solution.

Nuclear Particles The particles present in the nuclei of atoms. Upward of two dozen subatomic particles are known.

NUCLEAR PARTICLES (not a complete list)			
NAME	SYMBOL	CHARGE	MASS (AMU)
Proton	$_1H^1$	+1	1.00758
Neutron	$_0N^1$	0	1.00894
Alpha	$_2He^4$	+2	4.00280
Deuteron	$_1H^2$	+1	2.01416
Electron	$_{-1}E^0$	−1	0.00055
Positron	$_{+1}E^0$	+1	0.00055
Mesons	π		Between
	μ	0 or	electron
	τ	+1 or −1	and proton
	κ		mass
Neutrino	ν	0	less than
Antineutrino	$\bar{\nu}$		0.00005

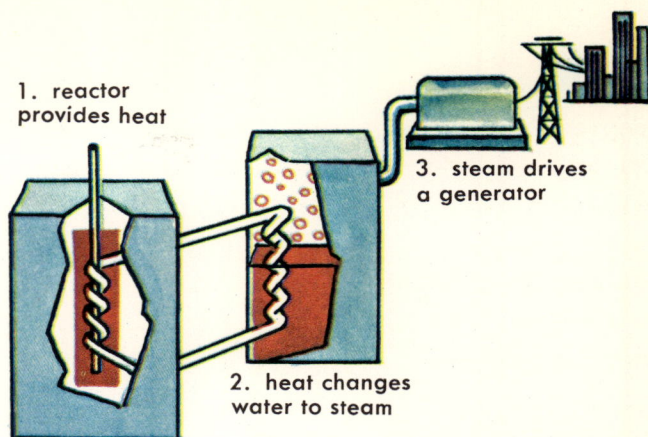

1. reactor provides heat
2. heat changes water to steam
3. steam drives a generator

Nuclear Reactor A device consisting of a fissile substance (see *Fission* and *Chain Reaction*) such as uranium, and a moderator such as heavy water or graphite, which controls the rate of energy release. The heat energy produced by the reactor produces power by converting water to steam.

Nucleus The central part, core. In an atom, the core which contains protons and neutrons.

Nylon (See section on *Synthetic Fibers*, p. 78.)

O

Octane A liquid hydrocarbon with the formula C_8H_{18}; member of the methane series (see *Homologous Series*).

Octane Number The measurement of the knock rating (see *Knocking*) of gasoline. Because iso-octane (2-2-4 trimethylpentane) burns evenly under high compression, it is given an octane number of 100. Normal heptane (C_7H_{16}), also an ingredient in gasoline, does not burn evenly (knocks) under high compression, so it is given an octane number of 0. Any gasoline that knocks to the same extent as a mixture of 90% iso-octane and 10% normal heptane is given an octane rating of 90. Octane rating, then, is the percentage by volume of iso-octane. High octane-rated gasoline is required for engines with high compression ratios.

Ore Any mineral containing metal.

Organic Living matter of all kinds.

Organic Chemistry Once defined as the chemistry of all living substances, but now defined as the chemistry of all carbon compounds, with the exception of the oxides of carbon and the metal carbonates.

Orlon (See section on *Synthetic Fibers,* p. 78.)

Oxidation In its broadest sense, any loss of electrons in a reaction. For example, when any substance combines with oxygen and, in the process, loses electrons.

Oxyacetylene Torch A device which produces a jet of acetylene gas mixed with oxygen. The mixture produces a flame of very high temperature (about 3300°C.). The oxyacetylene torch is used in welding.

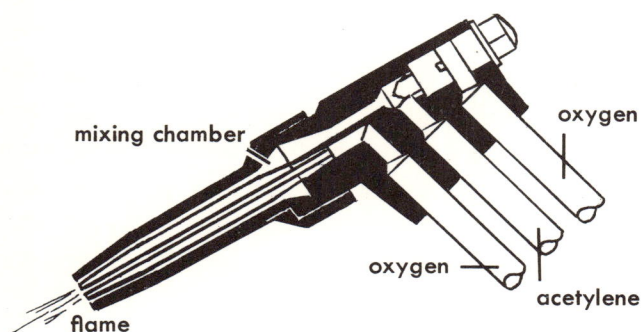

mixing chamber
oxygen
oxygen
acetylene
flame

Ozone An allotropic form of oxygen whose molecule is made up of 3 atoms of oxygen (O_3) rather than 2 (O_2), as in normal oxygen gas. Ozone is formed in the upper atmosphere as ultraviolet light acts on O_2 molecules. It is the odor erroneously called "burnt electricity" around electric motors and generators.

P

Paper Cellulose is obtained from wood pulp and pressed into thin flat sheets. At this stage the resulting paper is like blotting paper. To make it suitable as writing or drawing paper, various filler materials (such as clay) and binding materials (such as rosin soap) are added.

Paraffins The methane series of hydrocarbons having the general formula C_nH_{2n+2}. The early members of the series are gases (methane and ethane, for example), the middle members are liquids (the mineral oils), and the upper members are solids (forming paraffin wax, for example). (See *Homologous Series.*)

Pasteurization (of milk) Killing the bacteria but not their spores by boiling for 33 minutes at 143°F., or for 15 seconds at 160°F.

Peat Matted plant and animal decay laid down in swamps; the first stage in the formation of coal. When dried, peat can be burned.

Pepsin An enzyme that breaks down proteins in the stomach. (See also *Enzymes.*)

Periodic Law (See special section on *Chemical Laws,* p. 73.)

Periodic Table The chemical elements arranged in order of their atomic numbers in such a way that their properties may be predicted fairly accurately. (See p. 68.)

How paper is made: 1. pulpwood chips are carried to the "digester" which removes pulpy cellulose fibers; 2. pulp is washed to remove color; 3. wet paper is formed by adding water; 4. after drying, finished paper rolls off.

A "Christmas tree," forming the well head of today's oil wells, regulates the flow of crude oil and gases.

Petroleum   A mixture of hydrocarbons in the form of crude oil. (See *Fractionating Tower*.)

pH   The concentration of hydrogen ions in a solution. (See *pH Scale*.)

Phosgene   Carbonyl chloride—$COCl_2$. A poisonous gas with the odor of hay.

Phosphate   A natural rock which yields phosphate compounds valuable as a fertilizer. Animal bones also contain phosphate.

Photochemistry   The study of the action of light on matter.

Photosynthesis   The chemical action of green plants which, in the presence of sunlight, con-

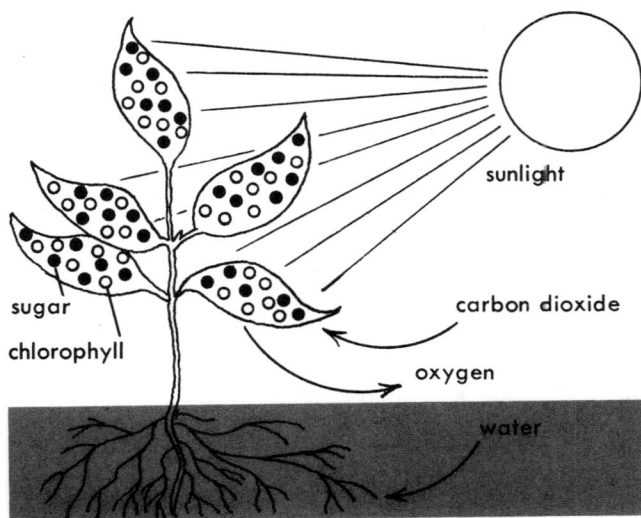

Photosynthesis: Carbon dioxide and water (with light and chlorophyll) produce sugar and oxygen.

vert carbon dioxide from the air, and water from the ground, into carbohydrates and oxygen. Chlorophyll in the plants acts as a catalyst in bringing about the following reaction:

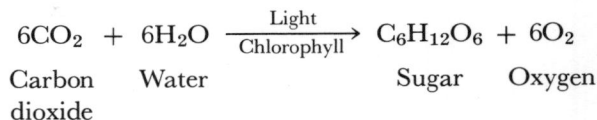

$$6CO_2 \ + \ 6H_2O \ \xrightarrow[\text{Chlorophyll}]{\text{Light}} \ C_6H_{12}O_6 \ + \ 6O_2$$

Carbon   Water   Sugar   Oxygen
dioxide

pH Scale   A scale ranging from 0 to 14, on which a solution's strength as an acid or base is indicated, based on .1N concentration. Seven is the neutral point on the scale and is occupied by water, which is neither acid nor base since its hydrogen (acid) ion balances its hydroxyl (base) ion—H^+OH^-. On the scale acids increase in strength from 7 to 0; bases increase in strength from 7 to 14. The difference in strength between any two consecutive pH entries amounts to a factor of ten; for example, an acid of pH 4 is ten times stronger than an acid of pH 5. Following are pH values of some common substances, ranging from acid to base: lemon—2.2-2.4; apple—2.9-3.3; orange—3.0-4.0; tomato—4.1-4.4; human saliva—6.0-7.6; blood—7.3-7.5.

	←Acid	Water	Base→	
0 1 2 3 4 5 6 **7** 8 9 10 11 12 13 14				
		Neutral point		

Physical Change   Any change in a substance not altering the chemical composition of the substance. Example: changing water into steam, or ice into water. (See also *Chemical Change*.)

Pig Iron   The iron produced when iron is separated from its ore in a blast furnace. Pig iron is about 92% iron, 4% carbon, 2.5% silicon, with traces of other elements. (See *Blast Furnace*.)

Pile, Uranium   (See *Nuclear Reactor*.)

Pitchblend An ore which contains uranium and radium.

Planetary Electrons (See *Electron Shells.*)

Plaster of Paris (See *Gypsum.*)

Plastics Natural or synthetic resins. Natural resins include such materials as rosin from pine trees, and amber, which is a fossil resin. These materials are hard, brittle, noncrystalline, and are not dissolved by water, but can be dissolved by organic solvents. The synthetic resins (called plastics) can be made soft by heat and then pressed or molded into any shape. **1. Thermoplastics**—materials that can be repeatedly softened by heat and hardened to any shape by cooling; Lucite, for example. **2. Thermosetting**—the process of making plastics by softening the material by heat and cooling it to

The heavy-duty plastics developed in recent years have a wide range of sturdy uses, among them boat hulls.

hardness only once; Bakelite is made this way. **3. Laminates**—a blend of two or more materials, such as plywood, Formica, Samsonite, which are light, strong, and durable. (See table of *Common Plastics,* p. 84.)

Plexiglas A highly transparent thermoplastic material also known as Lucite. It is more transparent than glass. Plexiglas is prepared from petroleum or natural gas, salt, coal, and water. (See table of *Common Plastics,* p. 84.)

Plumbago (See *Graphite.*)

Polar Bond A covalent chemical bond that gives a molecule a positive end and a negative

end. The gas HCl and water each has polar molecules. Example: if the atoms making up the water molecule were arranged in a straight line (H—O—H), the molecule would not have a positive end and a negative. But because the two hydrogen atoms are joined *to the same side* of the oxygen atom, the hydrogen end of the molecule tends to be more positive, while the oxygen end tends to be more negative. Because water molecules have charged ends, they can attract compounds with opposite charges. For this reason, water is an excellent dissolving substance. (See also *Nonpolar Bond* and *Chemical Bonds.*)

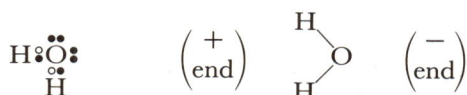

Polymerization The process of combining small molecules of the same or different compounds to produce large molecules of a new compound. **1. Condensation Polymerization**—the process of combining two monomers (small molecules) to form a polymer, during which water or some other substance is split out. For example, when two molecules of glycine (the monomers) are condensed (joined) to form glycylclycine (the polymer).

$$NH_2CH_2COOH + NH_2CH_2COOH \rightarrow$$

Glycine molecule   Glycine molecule

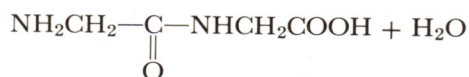

$$NH_2CH_2-\underset{\underset{O}{\|}}{C}-NHCH_2COOH + H_2O$$

Glycylclycine molecule   Water molecule

Still more water can be split out of this polymer to produce an even larger molecule. Nylon is an example of condensation polymerization. **2. Addition Polymerization**—the process of combining two or more monomers to form a polymer, without water or some other substance being split out. For example, when two molecules of acetylene combine to form the polymer vinylacetylene.

$$H-C\equiv C-H + H-C\equiv C-H \rightarrow H_2C=CH-C\equiv C-H$$

| Acetylene molecule | Acetylene molecule | Vinylacetylene molecule |

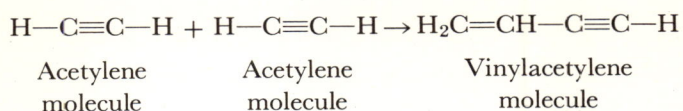

Still more acetylene molecules can be added onto the vinylacetylene polymer to produce a long chain. Neoprene (synthetic rubber) is an example of addition polymerization.

Polymers Large molecules formed by combining two or more smaller molecules (called monomers) in a process called polymerization. Nylon and proteins are both polymers.

Positron A subatomic particle with a positive charge. It is of the same mass as the electron and has a charge of the same strength as the electron.

Potash Potassium carbonate—K_2CO_3. A term loosely applied to all potassium salts, which are useful as fertilizers.

Precipitate An insoluble material produced during some chemical reactions. In equations, a precipitate is shown by an arrow pointing down ↓. For example, when hard water is boiled, calcium carbonate settles out as a precipitate as follows:

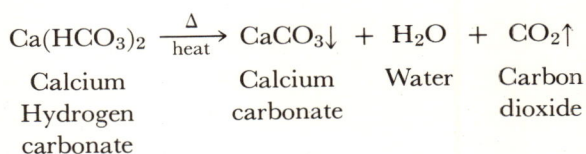

$$Ca(HCO_3)_2 \xrightarrow[\text{heat}]{\Delta} CaCO_3\downarrow + H_2O + CO_2\uparrow$$

| Calcium Hydrogen carbonate | Calcium carbonate | Water | Carbon dioxide |

Precipitation The production of a precipitate during chemical reaction.

Primary Cell (See *Battery*.)

Producer Gas A mixture of nitrogen and carbon monoxide; produced by passing air over hot coke.

Propane A flammable gas—C_3H_8. The third hydrocarbon in the methane, or paraffin, series. (See *Homologous Series*.)

Proteins Basic chemical units for all living things. They are giant molecules, all of which contain nitrogen, carbon, hydrogen, and oxygen. Some contain sulfur, phosphorus, iron, or other elements. The molecular weight of simple proteins ranges below and above 35,000. The complex proteins have molecular weights in the millions. Proteins are essential to living things because they are substances that go into tissue-building. Amino acids are the building blocks of proteins. Typical proteins: albumin (egg white), casein (cheese), gluten (wheat), and hemoglobin (blood). (See also table of *Foods*, p. 82.)

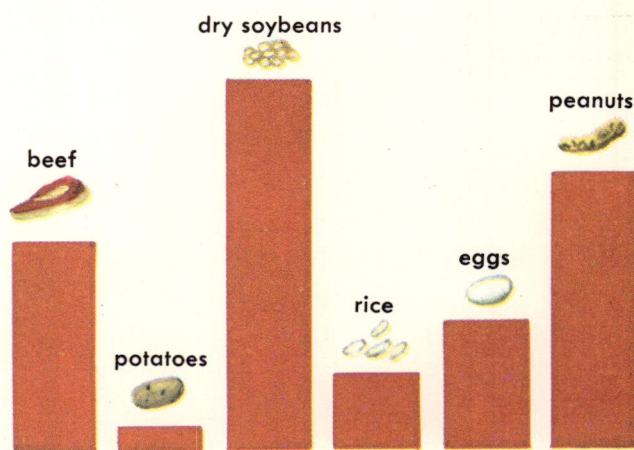

dry soybeans

peanuts

beef

eggs

rice

potatoes

This chart shows the relative protein value of six different foods in common use around the world.

Proton A positive unit of electricity in the nucleus of every atom. The charge of the proton is equal in strength to that of the electron, but its mass is 1840 times greater than the electron.

Ptyalin An enzyme in saliva; it changes starch into sugar. (See also *Enzymes*.)

Pyrex Glass which includes some boron. It expands and contracts only slightly when heated and cooled quickly, so it is an ideal material for beakers and other such equipment in chemistry laboratories. (See also *Glass*.)

Pyrites Sulfides of some metals. For example, "fool's gold" is copper pyrites—$CuFeS_2$, and iron pyrites—FeS_2.

Q

Qualitative (See *Analysis*.)

Quantitative (See *Analysis*.)

Quartz A clear or cloudy crystal composed of silica—SiO_2; called "rock crystal."

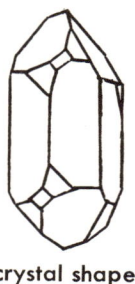

quartz crystal

crystal shape

Quenching The rapid cooling of red-hot steel or iron by dipping it in a water or oil bath. Such rapid cooling makes the hardest steel. Slow cooling produces a soft steel. (See also *Tempering*.)

Quicklime Calcium oxide—CaO. (See *Lime*.)

Quicksilver Mercury.

Quinine A bitter-tasting drug obtained from the bark of the cinchona tree—$C_{20}H_{24}O_2N_2$. This drug checks fever and chills caused by malaria. Quinine can be synthesized from a coal-tar product called benzaldehyde.

R

Radiation The giving off of subatomic particles, rays, or wave motion. (See *Alpha Rays, Beta Rays, Gamma Rays,* and *X rays*.)

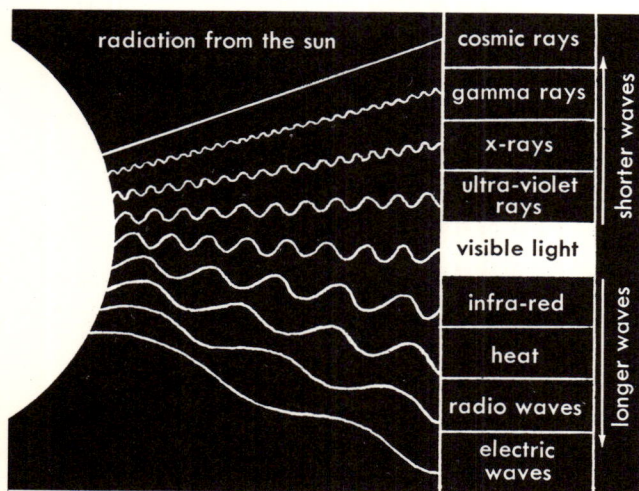

radiation from the sun

cosmic rays
gamma rays
x-rays
ultra-violet rays
visible light
infra-red
heat
radio waves
electric waves

shorter waves

longer waves

Radical A group of two or more elements that form a unit and that keep their group identity during many chemical reactions. The hydroxide radical is —OH; the sulfate radical is $=SO_4$; the ammonium radical is NH_4-.

Radioactive Disintegration When the atoms of a radioactive element change into atoms of a different element by emitting subatomic particles from their nuclei. For example, uranium[238] gives up an alpha particle (2 neutrons and 2 protons), thus changing into a new element of lower atomic weight, thorium[234]. The thorium[234] in turn gives up a beta particle (an electron), which causes one of its neutrons to change into a proton: the resulting new element is protactinium. Given enough time, our original uranium[238] sample will "disintegrate" and become stable lead (see table opposite).

Radioactivity The spontaneous decomposition of unstable elements, during which alpha particles, beta particles, or gamma rays are emitted. (See *Radioactive Disintegration*.)

Radiocarbon Carbon-14, a radioisotope of carbon formed when ordinary nitrogen captures a neutron. Carbon-14 has a half-life of about 5360 years. It emits beta particles. Because of its long half-life, it is useful in dating archeological specimens. For example, all living things contain a definite percentage of carbon-14. When the living substance dies it begins to lose its carbon-14, so by measuring the amount left in an Egyptian mummy, say, the age of the mummy can be told fairly accurately.

Radiocobalt Cobalt-60, a radioisotope of cobalt formed when metallic cobalt captures a neutron. Cobalt-60 has a half-life of 5.3 years. It emits gamma rays, hence is useful in medicine in killing cancer tissue.

Radioiodine Iodine-131, a product of fission with a half-life of 8 days. It emits gamma rays and is used in medicine to reduce activity of an

Radiation from the sun reaches us in many forms—from short-wave cosmic rays, through visible light and heat, to longer waves.

overactive thyroid gland. It is also useful in curing cancer of the thyroid. (Because iodine is attracted to the thyroid gland, all isotopes of iodine are also attracted.)

Radioisotopes Products of fission, or produced by bombarding the nuclei of certain atoms with a neutron. For example, radiosodium ($_{11}Na^{24}$) is formed by bombarding the nucleus of a normal sodium atom ($_{11}Na^{23}$) with a neutron. The new atom emits a beta particle (electron), and in the process one of its neutrons changes into a proton, producing an atom of magnesium, $_{12}Mg^{24}$. Radioisotopes have many uses in industry and medicine.

Radiophosphorus Phosphorus-32, a radioisotope formed when a normal sulfur atom captures a neutron. Radiophosphorus has a half-life of 14.3 days. It emits beta particles, reform-

ing sulfur. The isotope is used in medicine to treat leukemia; it is also used in agriculture to test the effectiveness of phosphorus as a fertilizer.

Radiosodium Sodium-24, a radioisotope formed when a normal sodium atom captures a neutron. Sodium-24 has a half-life of 15 hours. It emits beta particles and is used in medicine to investigate poor blood circulation.

Rare-Earth Elements Known as the "lanthanides," they are the group of 15 elements in the periodic table that begin with lanthanum (atomic number 57) and continue through lutetium (atomic number 71). All are rare metals and are very similar in properties.

Rayon (See special section on *Synthetic Fibers*, p. 78.)

THE TRANSMUTATION SERIES OF RADIOACTIVE ELEMENTS

ELEMENT	ATOMIC WEIGHT	NEUTRONS	ATOMIC NUMBER	PARTICLE EMITTED	HALF-LIFE*
Uranium ↓	238	146	92	α	4.5 billion years
Thorium ↓	234	144	90	β	24.6 days
Protactinium ↓	234	143	91	β	1.15 minutes
Uranium ↓	234	142	92	α	270,000 years
Thorium ↓	230	140	90	α	90,000 years
Radium ↓	226	138	88	α	1620 years
Radon ↓	222	136	86	α	3.82 days
Polonium ↓	218	134	84	α	3.05 minutes
Lead ↓	214	132	82	β	26.8 minutes
Bismuth ↓	214	131	83	β	19.7 minutes
Polonium ↓	214	130	84	α	.00015 seconds
Lead ↓	210	128	82	β	22 years
Bismuth ↓	210	127	83	β	5 days
Polonium ↓	210	126	84	α	140 days
Lead	206	124	82		Not radioactive (stable)

* Not all textbooks agree on the length of the half-life.

Reaction The combination of two or more substances resulting in the formation of a new product. (See *Chain Reaction, Chemical Change, Chemical Reaction, Double Displacement, Endothermic Reaction, Exothermic Reaction, Nuclear Reactor, Reversible Reaction.*)

Reactor (See *Nuclear Reactor.*)

Reagent Any chemical substance used in bringing about a chemical reaction.

Red Lead Minium—Pb_3O_4. An oxidizing agent; also a pigment used in the manufacture of glass.

Reduction In its broadest sense, any gain of electrons in a reaction. For example, when any substance containing oxygen is combined with hydrogen, or some other electropositive substance, and the oxygen is removed.

Relative Weight The weight of any atom in relation to the weight 16 assigned to the oxygen atom. (See *Atomic Weight.*)

Replacement (See *Displacement.*)

Replacement Series (See *Electromotive Series.*)

Residue The solid substance left on the filter paper after a solution has been filtered.

Reversible Reaction When two substances combine chemically and the new substances produced recombine into the original substances. For example, carbonic acid (H_2CO_3) when heated decomposes into carbon dioxide (CO_2) and water (H_2O); but the carbon dioxide dissolves in the water, reforming carbonic acid:

1. $H_2CO_3 \xrightarrow[\text{heat}]{\Delta} H_2O + CO_2$

2. $H_2O + CO_2 \rightarrow H_2CO_3$

Rubber **1. Natural Rubber**—made from a milky fluid, called latex, which comes from the *Hevea brasiliensis* tree. The latex is coagulated by the addition of a dilute acid, then the coagulated rubber is rolled into sheets and cured over fire. The next stage is to vulcanize the rubber (treat it with sulfur, which makes the

For special uses, certain synthetic rubbers are superior to natural rubber. Buna S is the most common synthetic.

rubber stable at relatively high and low temperatures). Unvulcanized rubber is sticky and soft at ordinary temperatures, and becomes brittle at low temperatures. **2. Synthetic Rubber**—produced in a variety of ways. Buna S rubber makes up about 80% of the synthetic rubber made in the United States today. It is a product of polymerization, coming from the two liquids butadiene and styrene. No single synthetic rubber is as good as natural rubber. However, some of the synthetic rubbers are superior to natural rubber for specialized purposes. The four leading synthetic rubbers are Buna S, Butyl, Perbunan, and Neoprene. (See table of *Synthetic Rubbers*, p. 78.)

Rust   The red deposit—hydrated oxide of iron ($FeO_3 \cdot H_2O$)—formed when iron is exposed to moist air and combines with the oxygen and water vapor of the air.

S

Saccharin   A white crystal about 550 times sweeter than sugar, but without food value, hence its use by people on diets. It can be harmful if taken excessively. Saccharin is made from toluene and has the formula $C_6H_4SO_2$-CONH.

Sal Ammoniac   Ammonium chloride, NH_4Cl.

Salt   Common salt is composed of crystals of sodium chloride—$NaCl$. A chemical salt is a substance formed when the hydrogen part of an acid is replaced by a metal. For example, when the metal copper replaces the hydrogen in sul-

The main corridor of a vast underground salt mine.

furic acid, the result being the salt copper sulfate.

Saltpeter   Potassium nitrate—KNO_3. Chilean saltpeter (sodium nitrate—$NaNO_3$) is the only plentiful nitrogen compound found in nature.

Sand   Small granules of silica—SiO_2.

Saturated Compound   A compound whose molecule has only single valence bonds linking its atoms. The hydrocarbons in the paraffin, or methane, series have such molecules with only single bonds linking the hydrogen and carbon atoms. For example:

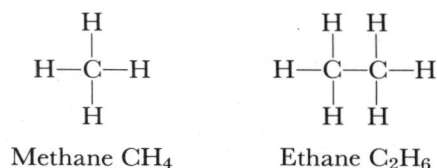

$$
\begin{array}{cc}
\begin{array}{c}
\text{H} \\
| \\
\text{H} - \text{C} - \text{H} \\
| \\
\text{H}
\end{array}
&
\begin{array}{c}
\text{H} \quad \text{H} \\
| \quad\;\; | \\
\text{H} - \text{C} - \text{C} - \text{H} \\
| \quad\;\; | \\
\text{H} \quad \text{H}
\end{array}
\\
\text{Methane } CH_4 & \text{Ethane } C_2H_6
\end{array}
$$

To build onto these molecules means substituting some other atom, or group, for a hydrogen atom; hence these saturated compounds are less reactive than compounds with double valence bonds, such as the ethylenes. (See also *Unsaturated Compound, Substitution Reaction*.)

Saturated Solution   A solution is saturated when it contains as much of a substance as it can hold at a constant temperature, in the presence of undissolved solute. (See also *Supersaturated Solution*.)

Sedimentation   The first stage in the purification of water. The water is run into tanks where it is mixed with aluminum sulfate and lime, forming a jellylike mass. The mass slowly sinks to the bottom of the tank, carrying with it most of the sediments and bacteria. (See *Water Purification* diagram.)

Slag   A cementlike material produced in a blast furnace when iron ore is smelted. Slag is formed when impurities in the iron ore combine with the limestone used in the smelting process.

Slaked Lime Calcium hydroxide—Ca(OH)$_2$. (See also *Lime*.)

Smelting Separating a metal from its ore by heating. (See *Blast Furnace*.)

Smoke Small particles of carbon suspended in the air. Nearly all of our industrial smoke consists of small particles of carbon. (See also *Cottrell Process*.)

Soap A metallic salt of a fatty acid. A mixture of fats and oils is fed into a tank of superheated water which converts the fats and oils into fatty acids. Next the fatty acids are purified by distillation. Sodium hydroxide (or potassium hydroxide for soft soaps) is next mixed with the fatty acids, the combination producing soap. During the process of making soap, glycerin is given off as a by-product.

Boiling fat is reduced to soap stock in a miniature tank. Periodic taste tests show the alkalinity level.

Soda Sodium compounds. (See *Bicarbonate of Soda, Baking Powder, Baking Soda,* and *Lye*.)

Soda Ash Sodium carbonate—Na$_2$CO$_3$; used in the manufacture of glass, paper, laundry soap, and as a water softener. (See *Hard Water*.)

Soda Lime (See *Lime*.)

Solid State Substances with a fixed shape, in which the molecules are firmly held together in a pattern by strong forces. The molecules mak-

ing up solids vibrate, while the molecules making up liquids and gases move about freely. (See also *Gaseous State*.)

Solubility The number of grams of a substance (solute) that can be dissolved in 100 g. of water (solvent) at a given temperature. Raising the temperature usually means an increase of solubility. (See *Solubility Table*, p. 88.)

Solute Any substance which is dissolved in a liquid to form a solution.

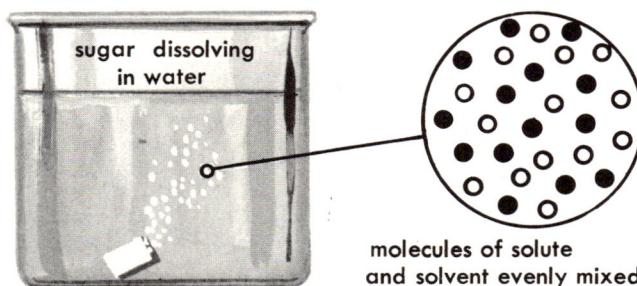

molecules of solute and solvent evenly mixed

Solution A mixture of a solute and a solvent; for example, when a cube of sugar (the solute) dissolves in water (the solvent). What happens is that the forces of attraction of the water molecules are stronger than the forces that hold the sugar crystals together. The sugar molecules then disperse, filling the spaces between the water molecules. A solution, then, can be thought of as an evenly dispersed mixture of two or more kinds of molecules.

Solvent Any substance that is able to dissolve another substance. Water is a solvent.

Specific Gravity (sp. gr.) The weight of a substance compared with an equal volume of water. For example, if a piece of marble weighs 100 g., we compare it with an equal volume of water and find that the water weighs 40 g. The marble, then, is 2.5 times heavier than the water, and this figure is the specific gravity of marble. Density is determined the same way, but is expressed in grams per cubic centimeter. Specific gravity is expressed as a pure number. (See *Density*.)

Specific Heat   (See *Heat.*)

Specific Volume   (See *Volume.*)

Spectroscope   1. Prism—an instrument fitted with a prism which separates the light reflected by a substance into its individual colors, or spectrum.   **2. Diffraction Grating**—a spectroscope fitted not with a prism but with a grooved polished-glass surface with as many as 15,000 grooves to the inch. When light from a substance falls on this grating, the different colors making up the light are reflected at different angles and so form a spectrum.

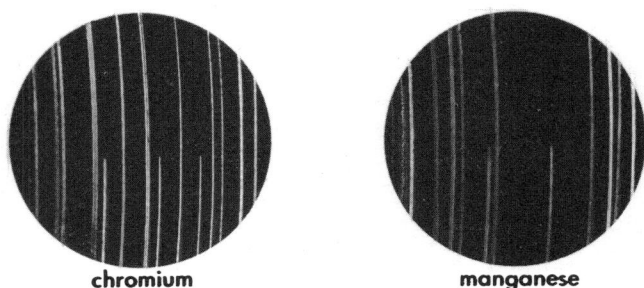

chromium   manganese

The characteristic spectrum patterns of chromium and manganese are shown in these diagrams.

Spectroscopic Analysis   The chemical composition of any substance is revealed by viewing its heated atoms through a spectroscope. Each element has a characteristic spectrum pattern.

Spontaneous Combustion   When a substance bursts into flame without the aid of a match or some other outside source of heat. Exposed to air in a poorly ventilated space, substances such as hay, oily rags, and grain dust generate their own heat. When they reach their kindling temperatures they burst into flame.

Stable   Any atom, molecule, or substance that does not decompose easily. A stable compound is one that is not easily decomposed by heat. (See also *Stable Elements.*)

Stable Elements   Those elements with relatively low atomic numbers. The elements ranging from hydrogen through calcium in the periodic table have about the same number of protons and neutrons in their nuclei; for example, oxygen has 8 protons and 8 neutrons. The elements beyond calcium begin to have increasingly more neutrons than protons; for example, uranium has 92 protons and 146 neutrons. This high neutron-proton ratio weakens the nuclear binding forces and causes the protons to repel each other. This results in the atom's disintegration. In elements which have about the same number of neutrons and protons, the binding forces within the nucleus are relatively strong, so the protons do not repel each other. (See also *Unstable Elements, Radioactive Disintegration.*)

Standard Conditions   (STP) Meaning standard temperature (0°C.) and standard pressure (760 mm. of mercury). (See also *Barometer.*)

Standard Pressure   The pressure that will support a column of mercury 760 mm. high.

Standard Solution   Any solution whose concentration is known.

Standard Temperature   0°C.

Starch   The storage carbohydrate of plants. Plants convert sugars into starch and store the starch granules within cellulose walls. When plant seeds germinate they use the stored starch by converting it back into sugar for food. Our chief source of commercial starch is the corn plant. Starch also comes from wheat and potatoes.

Steel   An alloy of iron. It consists of iron, a small amount of other metals, and carbon. Most steels have between 0.2% to 2.0% carbon. "Hard" steels have more carbon than "soft" steels. The way steels are heated and cooled also determines their hardness. (See also *Quenching* and *Tempering*, and table of *Alloys*, p. 76.)

STP   (See *Standard Conditions.*)

Structural Formula   (See *Formula*.)

Sublimation   Converting a solid directly to a vapor, without passing through the liquid phase; for example, dry ice does not melt, but evaporates.

Substitution Reaction   The reaction that occurs when an atom of one substance takes the place of one of the atoms making up a compound. For example, when a chlorine atom takes the place of one of the four hydrogen atoms in the methane molecule:

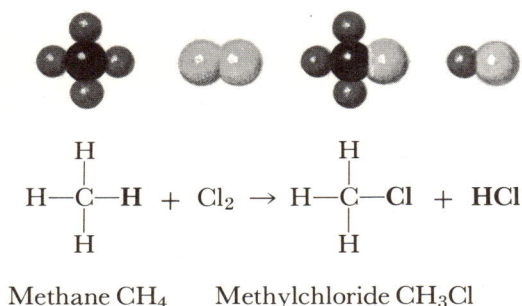

$$H-\underset{\underset{H}{|}}{\overset{\overset{H}{|}}{C}}-H \ + \ Cl_2 \ \rightarrow \ H-\underset{\underset{H}{|}}{\overset{\overset{H}{|}}{C}}-Cl \ + \ HCl$$

Methane CH_4 Methylchloride CH_3Cl

The second chlorine atom combines with the displaced hydrogen atom and forms a molecule of hydrogen chloride.

Sucrose $C_{12}H_{22}O_{11}$. Household sugar (cane sugar or beet sugar).

Sugar   A sweet-tasting carbohydrate. (See *Glucose, Grape Sugar, Lactose, Maltose, Sucrose*.)

Sulfur Dioxide SO_2. A colorless, choking gas. Industrially it is an important gas, since it is used in the manufacture of sulfuric acid. Sulfur dioxide can be prepared by burning sulfur (1), or by roasting iron pyrites (2).

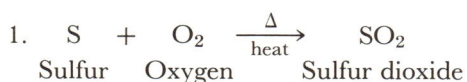

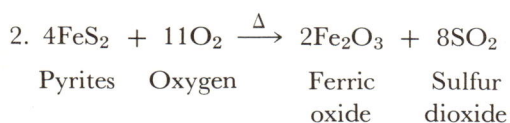

$$1. \quad S \ + \ O_2 \ \xrightarrow[\text{heat}]{\Delta} \ SO_2$$
$$\quad \text{Sulfur} \quad \text{Oxygen} \qquad \text{Sulfur dioxide}$$

$$2. \ 4FeS_2 \ + \ 11O_2 \ \xrightarrow{\Delta} \ 2Fe_2O_3 \ + \ 8SO_2$$
$$\quad \text{Pyrites} \quad \text{Oxygen} \qquad \text{Ferric} \quad \text{Sulfur}$$
$$\qquad\qquad\qquad\qquad\qquad \text{oxide} \quad \text{dioxide}$$

Sulfuric Acid H_2SO_4. The most widely used of all acids, and one of the most important industrial chemicals. It is used in making other chemicals. Sulfuric acid is used to prepare both nitric and hydrochloric acids. (See special section on *Acids*, p. 83.)

Supercooling   Lowering the temperature of a liquid below its freezing point. Under controlled conditions, supercooling will not necessarily solidify the liquid. But the addition of a crystal of the liquid, or any solid particle, will make the liquid freeze instantly. Distilled water, if not shaken or disturbed, can be cooled to $-3°C.$ (27°F.) without freezing.

Superheating   Heating a liquid above its boiling point.

Supersaturated Solution   A solution which contains a greater amount of solute than it would normally hold at a given temperature.

Surface Tension   The forces of attraction between the molecules making up the surface film of a liquid cause the surface to act as if it were a stretched sheet of rubber trying to contract. The tension produced makes it possible to float a dry razor blade or a dry needle in a dish of water. It is surface tension that permits certain insects to run along the surface of a pond. Detergents and other wetting agents destroy surface tension.

A relatively tough skin (surface tension) holds liquid droplets in the form of spheres.

Suspension   The fine distribution of one state of matter throughout another state of matter; clay in water and smoke in air are both suspensions. (See also *Colloidal State*.) Suspensions may be coarse and settle out rapidly, or they may be fine.

Synthesis   Constructing or building a compound by adding simple parts to it. For example, water can be synthesized by passing hydrogen over heated cupric oxide. The hydrogen combines with the oxygen in the cupric oxide, leaving copper.

$$H_2 + Cu_2O \rightarrow 2Cu + H_2O$$

Synthetic Rubber   (See *Rubber*.)

T

Tar   (See *Coal Tar*.)

Tarnishing   The formation of an oxide or sulfide on the surface of a metal, destroying its luster. Traces of hydrogen sulfide (H_2S) in the air react with the silver coating of silverware and produce a dark coating of silver sulfide.

$$2Ag + H_2S \rightarrow Ag_2S + H_2\uparrow$$

Temperature   The measurement of the intensity of heat, expressed in units called "degrees." The temperature of a body depends on how quickly or slowly its atoms and molecules are moving about. (See also *Heat, Absolute Scale, Centigrade Scale, Fahrenheit Scale, Thermometer*.)

Tempering   Heating steel to a definite temperature, then cooling it by quenching. This process brings the steel to the desired state of hardness. (See also *Quenching*.)

Ternary   Meaning three. A ternary compound is one made up of three elements. For example, chloroform, which is made up of carbon, hydrogen, and chlorine—$CHCl_3$.

Thermite   A mixture of aluminum powder and the oxide of a metal—for example, iron oxide. When the two are combined, much heat is given off and the iron melts. Thermite is an excellent welding material.

SOME INTERESTING TEMPERATURES

DEGREES CENTIGRADE	WHAT HAPPENS
−273.18	Absolute zero
−272.2	Helium melts
−268.9	Helium boils
−259.2	Hydrogen melts
−252.8	Hydrogen boils
−218.4	Oxygen melts
−209.9	Nitrogen melts
−195.8	Nitrogen boils
−183	Oxygen boils
−114.5	Grain alcohol freezes
−78.5	Carbon dioxide turns solid
−38.8	Mercury freezes
−33.4	Ammonia boils
−10	Sulfur dioxide boils
0	Ice melts and water freezes
20	Room temperature
37	Body temperature
60	Wood's metal melts
78.4	Grain alcohol boils
100	Water boils
112.8	Sulfur (rhombic) melts
170	Sugar melts
231.8	Tin melts
327.3	Lead melts
419.4	Zinc melts
444.6	Sulfur boils
550	Red heat becomes visible
660	Aluminum melts
800	Table salt melts
961	Silver melts
1000	Bright-red heat
1068	Gold melts
1083	Copper melts
1200	Yellow heat
1350	White heat
1453	Nickel melts
1470	Quartz melts
1535	Iron melts
1600	Sand melts
1769	Platinum melts
2700	Oxyacetylene flame
3380	Tungsten melts
3500	Carbon melts
4000	Electric arc
6000	Sun's surface
20,000,000	Sun's interior (temperature needed for fusion)

Thermometer   A device which measures the intensity of heat. As the liquid in a thermometer expands, its increase in volume can be read off a scale marked in degrees of temperature. Mercury is used in laboratory and clinical thermometers. As the liquid mercury is heated, it expands and rises in a capillary (hairlike) tube. For outdoor use, particularly in regions of intense cold, alcohol is preferable to mercury, since alcohol has a lower freezing point.

Thermoplastic   (See *Plastics*.)

Thermosetting   (See *Plastics*.)

Titration   A method of discovering the concentration (strength) of an unknown solution by making it react with a definite amount of a known (standard) solution.

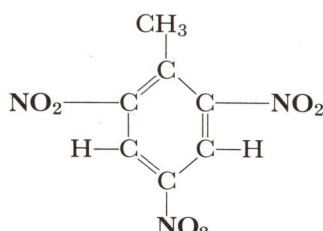

TNT   Trinitrotoluene—$C_7H_5(NO_2)_3$. An explosive prepared by substituting 3 nitro (NO_2) groups for 3 of the hydrogen atoms in the toluene molecule.

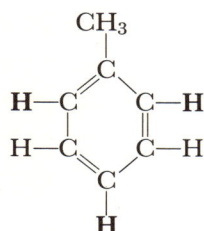

Toluene C_7H_8

Trinitrotoluene $C_7H_5(NO_2)_3$

Tracers   Radioisotopes which emit radiation and which are used in medicine and industry. For example, a solution of radiosodium chloride can be used to trace blood circulation. A small amount of this radioisotope is injected into a vein in the arm. If the person's circulation is normal, it will take a "normal" length of time for the radioisotope to be carried by the blood stream to the foot, where it can be detected with a Geiger counter. Blood clots can also be located by radioactive tracers. (See also *Radioisotopes*.)

Transmutation of Elements   The change of one element into another element through the loss or gain of nuclear particles. (See *Radioactive Disintegration*.)

Triple Bond   When three electron pairs are shared to join atoms in a compound. Double- and triple-bond compounds are more active than single-bond compounds. (See p. 18.)

Tyndall Effect   (See *Colloidal State*.)

U

Ultramicroscope   An instrument which can bring a beam of light into sharp focus in a solution containing colloidal particles, making the particles visible as pinpoints of light. Without the aid of the sharply focused light beam, the particles are too small to be seen with an ordinary microscope.

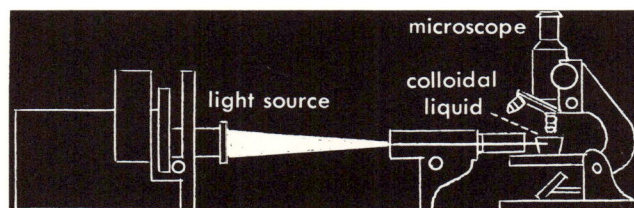

The individual particles making up a colloidal solution appear as pinpoints of light in the ultramicroscope.

Ultraviolet Rays   Electromagnetic waves shorter than visible light waves, but longer than X rays.

Unsaturated Compound   A compound whose molecule has a double or triple bond: that is, a "spare" valency bond ready to link up with an outside atom or group. These "spare" valency bonds make the unsaturated compounds more reactive than the saturated compounds (which do not have such spare bonds). The unsaturated compounds react by "addition," while the saturated compounds react by "substitution." The ethylenes are an example of unsaturated compounds with double bonds. For example, when bromine is added to ethylene, the double valency bond linking the carbon atoms becomes two single bonds, each one accepting a bromine atom:

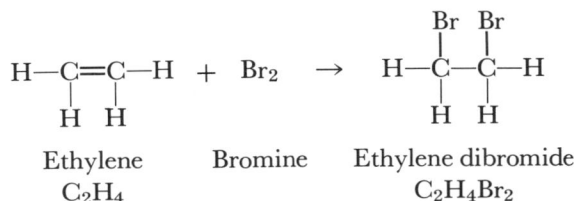

$$H-\underset{\underset{H}{|}}{C}=\underset{\underset{H}{|}}{C}-H \;+\; Br_2 \;\rightarrow\; H-\underset{\underset{H}{|}}{\overset{\overset{Br}{|}}{C}}-\underset{\underset{H}{|}}{\overset{\overset{Br}{|}}{C}}-H$$

Ethylene C_2H_4 Bromine   Ethylene dibromide $C_2H_4Br_2$

Hydrogen can be added to ethylene the same way, producing ethane:

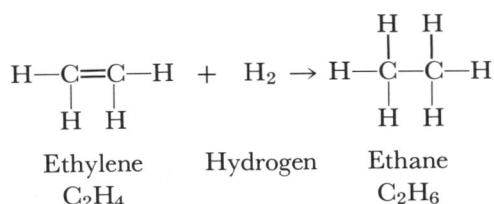

$$H-\underset{\underset{H}{|}}{C}=\underset{\underset{H}{|}}{C}-H \;+\; H_2 \;\rightarrow\; H-\underset{\underset{H}{|}}{\overset{\overset{H}{|}}{C}}-\underset{\underset{H}{|}}{\overset{\overset{H}{|}}{C}}-H$$

Ethylene C_2H_4 Hydrogen   Ethane C_2H_6

Unstable The characteristic of an atom, molecule, or substance that permits the atom, molecule, or substance to decompose easily. (See *Unstable Elements*.)

Unstable Elements Those elements with relatively high atomic numbers and whose nuclei contain substantially more neutrons than protons. This "excess" of neutrons causes the protons to repel each other, resulting in the gradual disintegration of the atom. (See also *Radioactive Disintegration, Stable Elements*.)

Uranium Series (See *Radioactive Disintegration* and table, p. 57.)

Urea An organic compound—$CO(NH_2)_2$. It was the first organic compound to be synthesized, and is made by the reaction of ammonia with carbon dioxide at high temperature and high pressure. Urea is valuable as a fertilizer, and is used in plastics and textile fibers.

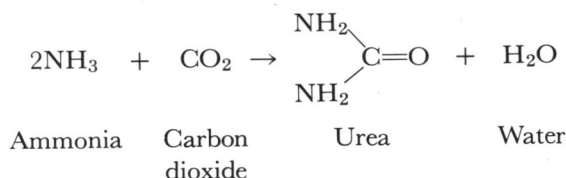

$$2NH_3 \;+\; CO_2 \;\rightarrow\; \underset{NH_2}{\overset{NH_2}{C}}{=}O \;+\; H_2O$$

Ammonia   Carbon dioxide   Urea   Water

V

Valence The ability of one atom to combine with another atom to form a compound. The number of bonds an atom has determines the number of other atoms it can combine with. For example, because one atom of oxygen has two bonds, it combines with two atoms of hydrogen (which has only one bond per atom). The valence of oxygen is said to be 2. Valence bonds are electrical forces that exist between atoms and hold atoms together in a molecule. (See also *Chemical Bonds*.)

Vapor A gas which is below its critical temperature.

Vapor Pressure The pressure of the vapor molecules suspended above a liquid contained in a closed space. A pot lid dances up and down as the vapor pressure becomes high. What happens is that more and more water molecules are turning into vapor molecules. When a liquid and its vapor are exchanging molecules at an even rate, the two are said to be in "equilibrium"; for example, when the vapor molecules are changing into liquid molecules at the same rate as the liquid molecules are changing into vapor molecules. A rise in temperature will upset the equilibrium and increase the vapor pressure. (See also *Boiling*.)

VAPOR PRESSURE OF WATER*			
TEMP. °C.	PRESSURE (mm. of Hg)	TEMP. °C.	PRESSURE (mm. of Hg)
0	5	24	22
5	7	25	24
10	9	26	25
11	10	27	27
12	11	28	28
13	11	29	30
14	12	30	32
15	13	40	55
16	14	50	93
17	15	60	149
18	16	70	234
19	17	80	355
20	18	90	526
21	19	100	760
22	20	110	1075

* To the nearest whole number

Vinegar A solution of 3% to 6% acetic acid.

Viscosity The tendency of a liquid to resist flowing. Hot tar and molasses are viscous.

Vitamins Organic substances which are present in food and which are needed in small amounts to avoid diseases of deficiency. So far as we know, the body cannot manufacture vitamins: it must obtain them from the outside. (See table of *Vitamins,* p. 81.)

Volatile Easily vaporized. Substances with high vapor pressure are volatile. (See also *Vapor Pressure, Boiling.*)

Volume 1. A measure of the space a substance occupies. 2. **Specific Volume**—the volume which one gram of a substance occupies at a definite temperature and pressure.

Vulcanite A hard substance resulting when rubber combines with sulfur.

Vulcanize Heating natural rubber with sulfur to make it stable at relatively high and low temperatures. (See *Rubber.*)

W

Washing Soda Sodium carbonate with water of crystallization—$Na_2CO_3 \cdot 10H_2O$.

Water Gas A fuel gas made by forcing steam over a bed of hot coke, producing a mixture of carbon monoxide and hydrogen. This mixture is water gas.

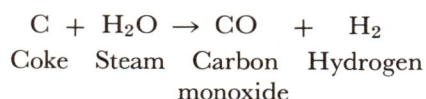

$$C + H_2O \rightarrow CO + H_2$$
Coke Steam Carbon Hydrogen
monoxide

Water of Crystallization A definite number of water molecules joined with various substances in the crystal state. Washing soda, for example, has 10 molecules of water of crystallization, and is written $Na_2CO_3 \cdot 10H_2O$. Copper-sulfate crystals contain 5 molecules of water of crystallization—$CuSO_4 \cdot 5H_2O$.

Water of Hydration The same as *Water of Crystallization.*

Water Purification To make water safe for drinking, it is passed through several processes which make it clear, soft, "fresh"-smelling and

Five stages in a typical water purification system of a city are shown in the step-by-step diagrams on this page.

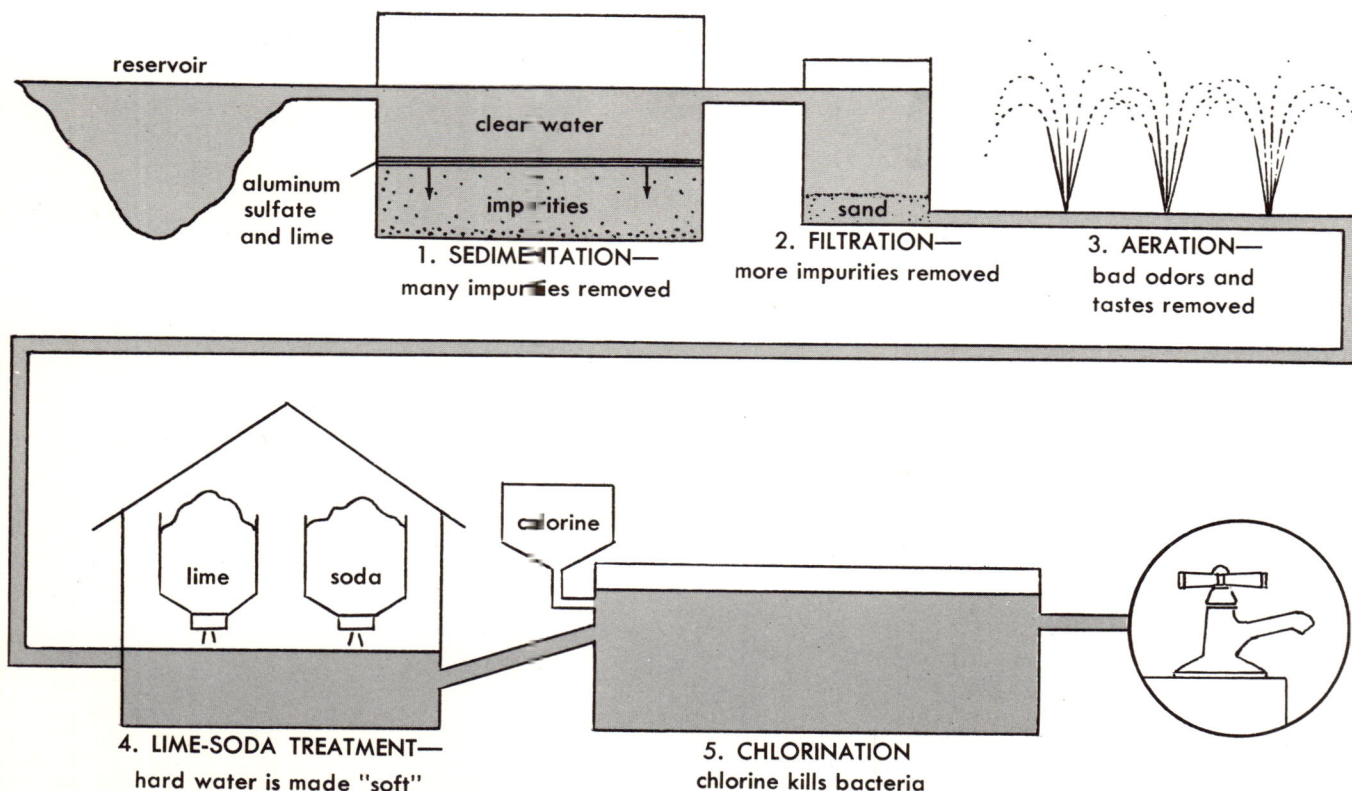

reservoir

clear water

aluminum sulfate and lime

impurities

1. SEDIMENTATION—
many impurities removed

sand

2. FILTRATION—
more impurities removed

3. AERATION—
bad odors and tastes removed

lime soda

chlorine

4. LIME-SODA TREATMENT—
hard water is made "soft"

5. CHLORINATION
chlorine kills bacteria

tasting, and free from harmful bacteria. The purifying stages include **1. Sedimentation, 2. Filtration, 3. Aeration, 4. Lime-Soda Treatment, 5. Chlorination.** Water-purification systems may differ from place to place. (See separate entries for each of these five stages.)

Welding Joining two metals by heating them until they melt and fuse. (See *Oxyacetylene Torch* and *Thermite.*)

Wood Alcohol (See *Alcohol.*)

Wood Gas The gas given off during the destructive distillation of wood. (See *Destructive Distillation.*)

Wood Tar A substance produced by the destructive distillation of wood. It is used to protect wood from termites. (See *Destructive Distillation.*)

Wrought Iron Iron which has a considerable amount of slag, which makes it very tough; used in grillwork and radiators.

X

X rays The rays sent out by a material object when a stream of cathode rays (electrons) strikes it. These rays are quite like visible light, but of a much shorter wave-length. Although X rays can penetrate flesh, they are stopped by bone, hence we can make X-ray photographs (called radiographs). X rays are also called "Roentgen rays."

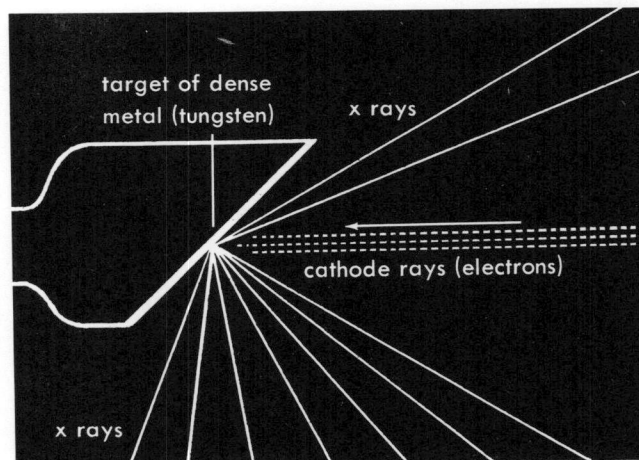

A target of dense metal, such as tungsten, gives off X rays when struck by a stream of electrons.

THE PERIODIC TABLE OF THE ELEMENTS

The periodic table of the elements was pioneered by the Russian chemist Dmitri Mendeleev, the British chemist John Newlands, and the German chemist Julius Meyer. The periodic table tells us many things about the properties of related elements.

First of all, if you read the table along the horizontal columns (called "periods") from left to right, you will see that the elements are arranged according to their atomic number. If you read the table from top to bottom, you will find that the elements along any one vertical column have similar properties. For example, the elements in the far left column are very active, light metals with low melting points, and have only a single electron in their outer

	1 — 1.0080 HYDROGEN — H — 2

ALKALI METALS — Group 1a	ALKALINE EARTH METALS — Group 2a	Group 3a	Group 4a	Group 5a	Group 6a	Group 7a	Group 8	
3 — 6.940 LITHIUM — Li — 2	4 — 9.013 BERYLLIUM — Be — 1							
11 — 22.991 SODIUM — Na — 1	12 — 24.32 MAGNESIUM — Mg — 3							
19 — 39.100 POTASSIUM — K — 2	20 — 40.08 CALCIUM — Ca — 6	21 — 44.96 SCANDIUM — Sc — 1	22 — 47.90 TITANIUM — Ti — 5	23 — 50.95 VANADIUM — V — 2	24 — 52.01 CHROMIUM — Cr — 4	25 — 54.94 MANGANESE — Mn — 1	26 — 55.85 IRON — Fe — 4	27 — 58.94 COBALT — Co — 1
37 — 85.48 RUBIDIUM — Rb — 1	38 — 87.63 STRONTIUM — Sr — 4	39 — 88.92 YTTRIUM — Y — 1	40 — 91.22 ZIRCONIUM — Zr — 5	41 — 92.91 NIOBIUM — Nb — 1	42 — 95.95 MOLYBDENUM — Mo — 7	43 — [99] TECHNETIUM — Tc	44 — 101.1 RUTHENIUM — Ru — 7	45 — 102.91 RHODIUM — Rh — 1
55 — 132.91 CESIUM — Cs — 1	56 — 137.36 BARIUM — Ba — 7	57–71 Rare Earths	72 — 178.60 HAFNIUM — Hf — 6	73 — 180.95 TANTALUM — Ta — 1	74 — 183.92 TUNGSTEN — W — 5	75 — 186.31 RHENIUM — Re — 1	76 — 190.2 OSMIUM — Os — 7	77 — 192.2 IRIDIUM — Ir — 2
87 — [223] FRANCIUM — Fr	88 — 226.05 RADIUM — Ra							

RARE EARTHS ▶

Group 3a	Group 4a	Group 5a	Group 6a	Group 7a	Group 8	
57 — 138.92 LANTHANUM — La — 2	58 — 140.13 CERIUM — Ce — 4	59 — 140.92 PRASEODYMIUM — Pr — 1	60 — 144.27 NEODYMIUM — Nd — 7	61 — [145] PROMETHIUM — Pm	62 — 150.43 SAMARIUM — Sm — 6	63 — 152.0 EUROPIUM — Eu — 2
89 — [227] ACTINIUM — Ac	90 — 232.05 THORIUM — Th	91 — 231 PROTACTINIUM — Pa	92 — 238.07 URANIUM — U	93 — [237] NEPTUNIUM — Np	94 — [242] PLUTONIUM — Pu	95 — [243] AMERICIUM — Am

shell. The elements in the second major column have two electrons in their outer shell. By the time you reach the far right you find that all of the elements in that column are gases with full outer shells, which means that they are inactive elements, hence they are called the "inert gases." (See page 31.)

Reading down the columns you will notice that the atomic weights of the elements increase. As the atomic weight increases within a group of metals, the activity *decreases;* for example, in the left column cesium (Cs) is less active than lithium (Li). With the nonmetals, however, the reverse is true. As the atomic weight increases, the activity of the nonmetal also *increases.*

INERT GASES

Group 0

	Group 3b	Group 4b	Group 5b	Group 6b	Group 7b	2 4.003 HELIUM **He** 2
	5 10.82 BORON **B** 2	6 12.011 CARBON **C** 2	7 14.008 NITROGEN **N** 2	8 16.000 OXYGEN **O** 3	9 19.00 FLUORINE **F** 1	10 20.183 NEON **Ne** 3
	13 26.98 ALUMINUM **Al** 1	14 28.09 SILICON **Si** 3	15 30.975 PHOSPHORUS **P** 1	16 32.066 SULFUR **S** 4	17 35.457 CHLORINE **Cl** 2	18 39.944 ARGON **A** 3

Group 1b	Group 2b						
28 58.71 NICKEL **Ni** 5	29 63.54 COPPER **Cu** 2	30 65.38 ZINC **Zn** 5	31 69.72 GALLIUM **Ga** 2	32 72.60 GERMANIUM **Ge** 5	33 74.91 ARSENIC **As** 1	34 78.96 SELENIUM **Se** 6	35 79.916 BROMINE **Br** 2
46 106.4 PALLADIUM **Pd** 6	47 107.880 SILVER **Ag** 2	48 112.41 CADMIUM **Cd** 8	49 114.76 INDIUM **In** 2	50 118.70 TIN **Sn** 10	51 121.76 ANTIMONY **Sb** 2	52 127.61 TELLURIUM **Te** 8	53 126.91 IODINE **I** 1
78 195.23 PLATINUM **Pt** 6	79 197.0 GOLD **Au** 1	80 200.61 MERCURY **Hg** 7	81 204.39 THALLIUM **Tl** 2	82 207.21 LEAD **Pb** 4	83 209.00 BISMUTH **Bi** 1	84 210 POLONIUM **Po**	85 [211] ASTATINE **At**

(Krypton 36 83.80 **Kr** 6; Xenon 54 131.30 **Xe** 9; Radon 86 222 **Rn**)

64 156.9 GADOLINIUM **Gd** 7	65 158.93 TERBIUM **Tb** 1	66 162.51 DYSPROSIUM **Dy** 7	67 164.94 HOLMIUM **Ho** 1	68 167.27 ERBIUM **Er** 6	69 168.94 THULIUM **Tm** 1	70 173.04 YTTERBIUM **Yb** 7	71 174.99 LUTETIUM **Lu** 1
96 [245] CURIUM **Cm**	97 [245] BERKELIUM **Bk**	98 [248] CALIFORNIUM **Cf**	99 [253] EINSTEINIUM **Es**	100 [252] FERMIUM **Fm**	101 [256] MENDELEVIUM **Md**	102 [254] NOBELIUM **No**	103 [about 257] LAWRENCIUM **Lw**

THE ELEMENTS

SYMBOL OF ELEMENT	ATOMIC NUMBER / NAME ATOMIC WEIGHT	DATE DISCOVERED	SYMBOL OF ELEMENT	ATOMIC NUMBER / NAME ATOMIC WEIGHT	DATE DISCOVERED
Ac	89 Actinium [227]	1899	Er	68 Erbium 167.27	1843
Al	13 Aluminum 26.98	1827	Eu	63 Europium 152.0	1901
Am	95 Americium [243]	1944	Fm	100 Fermium [252]	1953
Sb	51 Antimony 121.76	1604	F	9 Fluorine 19.00	1886
A	18 Argon 39.944	1894	Fr	87 Francium [223]	1939
As	33 Arsenic 74.91	(ancient)	Gd	64 Gadolinium 156.9	1880
At	85 Astatine [211]	1940	Ga	31 Gallium 69.72	1875
Ba	56 Barium 137.36	1808	Ge	32 Germanium 72.60	1886
Bk	97 Berkelium [245]	1949	Au	79 Gold 197.0	(ancient)
Be	4 Beryllium 9.013	1798	Hf	72 Hafnium 178.60	1923
Bi	83 Bismuth 209.00	(ancient)	He	2 Helium 4.003	1895
B	5 Boron 10.82	1808	Ho	67 Holmium 164.94	1878
Br	35 Bromine 79.916	1826	H	1 Hydrogen 1.0080	1790
Cd	48 Cadmium 112.41	1817	In	49 Indium 114.76	1824
Ca	20 Calcium 40.08	1808	I	53 Iodine 126.91	1811
Cf	98 Californium [248]	1950	Ir	77 Iridium 192.2	1804
C	6 Carbon 12.011	(ancient)	Fe	26 Iron 55.85	(ancient)
Ce	58 Cerium 140.13	1803	Kr	36 Krypton 83.80	1898
Cs	55 Cesium 132.91	1860	La	57 Lanthanum 138.92	1839
Cl	17 Chlorine 35.457	1774	Lw	103 Lawrencium (about 257)	1961
Cr	24 Chromium 52.01	1798	Pb	82 Lead 207.21	(ancient)
Co	27 Cobalt 58.94	1737	Li	3 Lithium 6.940	1817
Cu	29 Copper 63.54	(ancient)	Lu	71 Lutetium 174.99	1907
Cm	96 Curium [245]	1944	Mg	12 Magnesium 24.32	1808
Dy	66 Dysprosium 162.51	1886	Mn	25 Manganese 54.94	1774
E	99 Einsteinium [253]	1952	Mv	101 Mendelevium [256]	1955

THE ELEMENTS

SYMBOL OF ELEMENT	ATOMIC NUMBER NAME ATOMIC WEIGHT	DATE DISCOVERED	SYMBOL OF ELEMENT	ATOMIC NUMBER NAME ATOMIC WEIGHT	DATE DISCOVERED
Hg	80 Mercury 200.61	(ancient)	Sm	62 Samarium 150.43	1879
Mo	42 Molybdenum 95.95	1781	Sc	21 Scandium 44.96	1879
Nd	60 Neodymium 144.27	1885	Se	34 Selenium 78.96	1818
Ne	10 Neon 20.183	1898	Si	14 Silicon 28.09	1824
Np	93 Neptunium [237]	1940	Ag	47 Silver 107.880	(ancient)
Ni	28 Nickel 58.71	1751	Na	11 Sodium 22.991	1807
Nb	41 Niobium 92.91	1801	Sr	38 Strontium 87.63	1808
N	7 Nitrogen 14.008	1772	S	16 Sulfur 32.066	(ancient)
No	102 Nobelium 254	1957	Ta	73 Tantalum 180.95	1802
Os	76 Osmium 190.2	1804	Tc	43 Technetium [99]	1937
O	8 Oxygen 16.000	1774	Te	52 Tellurium 127.61	1783
Pd	46 Palladium 106.4	1803	Tb	65 Terbium 158.93	1843
P	15 Phosphorus 30.975	1669	Tl	81 Thallium 204.39	1861
Pt	78 Platinum 195.23	1748	Th	90 Thorium 232.05	1829
Pu	94 Plutonium [242]	1940	Tm	69 Thulium 168.94	1879
Po	84 Polonium 210	1898	Sn	50 Tin 118.70	(ancient)
K	19 Potassium 39.100	1807	Ti	22 Titanium 47.90	1791
Pr	59 Praseodymium 140.92	1885	W	74 Tungsten 183.92	1783
Pm	61 Promethium [145]	1947	U	92 Uranium 238.07	1789
Pa	91 Protactinium 231	1917	V	23 Vanadium 50.95	1830
Ra	88 Radium 226.05	1898	Xe	54 Xenon 131.30	1898
Rn	86 Radon 222	1900	Yb	70 Ytterbium 173.04	1878
Re	75 Rhenium 186.31	1925	Y	39 Yttrium 88.92	1794
Rh	45 Rhodium 102.91	1803	Zn	30 Zinc 65.38	(ancient)
Rb	37 Rubidium 85.48	1861	Zr	40 Zirconium 91.22	1789
Ru	44 Ruthenium 101.1	1844			

NAMING COMPOUNDS

Following are a few simple keys which will help you to understand something of the composition of certain compounds by analyzing their names.

mono....means one; e.g., carbon **mon**oxide (CO).
di......means two; e.g., carbon **di**oxide (CO_2).
tri.....means three; e.g., sulfur **tri**oxide (SO_3).
tetra...means four; e.g., silicon **tetra**fluoride (SiF_4).
pent....means five; e.g., phosphorus **pent**oxide (P_2O_5).
Etc.
poly....means many.

.......**ous**—means an element's lower combining number. In the case of iron of valence 2, it is ferr**ous** chloride ($FeCl_2$).

.........**ic**—means an element's higher combining number. In the case of iron of valence 3, it is ferr**ic** chloride ($FeCl_3$).

ACIDS

hydro....**ic**—means a two-element acid; e.g., **hydro**chlor**ic** acid (HCl), which contains hydrogen and chlorine.

.........**ic**—without "hydro" means a three-element acid; e.g., sulfur**ic** acid (H_2SO_4), which contains hydrogen, sulfur, and oxygen.

......**ous**—means a three-element acid which contains one less oxygen atom than an **ic** acid; e.g., sulfur**ous** acid (H_3SO_3).

hypo....**ous**—means a three-element acid with two fewer oxygen atoms; e.g., **hypo**sulfur**ous** acid (H_2SO_2).

per.......**ic**—means a three-element acid which contains one more oxygen atom than an **ic** acid; e.g., **per**chlor**ic** acid ($HClO_4$).

Acids with the prefix **ortho** (in **ortho**phosphoric acid—H_3PO_4) have one more molecule of water than acids with the prefix **meta** (in **meta**phosphoric acid—HPO_3).

SALTS

hypo and **per**—are used to designate salts in the same way as they are used to designate acids.

.........**ide**—salts are formed from **hydro**.....**ic** acids; e.g., sodium chlor**ide** (NaCl).

.........**ate**—salts are formed from **ic** acids; e.g., sodium sulf**ate** (Na_2SO_4).

.........**ite**—salts are formed from **ous** acids; e.g., sodium sulf**ite** (Na_2SO_3).

IMPORTANT LAWS IN CHEMISTRY

Boyle's Law: When Robert Boyle experimented with gases, he discovered that if he doubled the pressure on a gas, the volume of the gas was reduced one-half. His gas law is stated: **The volume of a given mass of [dry] gas varies inversely with the pressure, provided the temperature remains unchanged.**

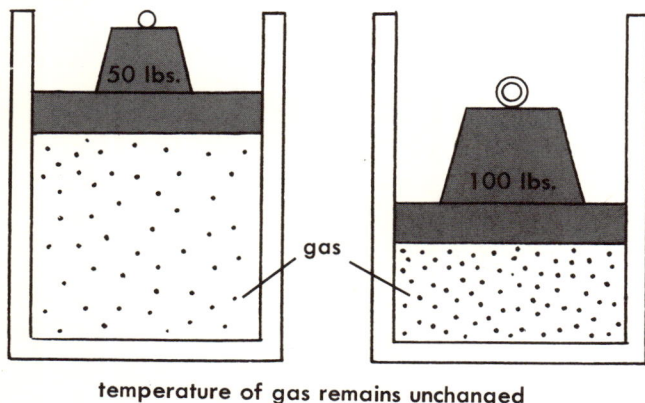

temperature of gas remains unchanged

Charles' Law: In his research on gases, Charles discovered that if he raised the temperature of a gas, the volume of the gas increased. We know that this increased volume results from the more rapid motion of the gas molecules; more space is created between the molecules, and it is this increase in space that we call volume. Charles' law is stated: **The volume of a gas varies with its absolute temperature [provided that the pressure remains unchanged].**

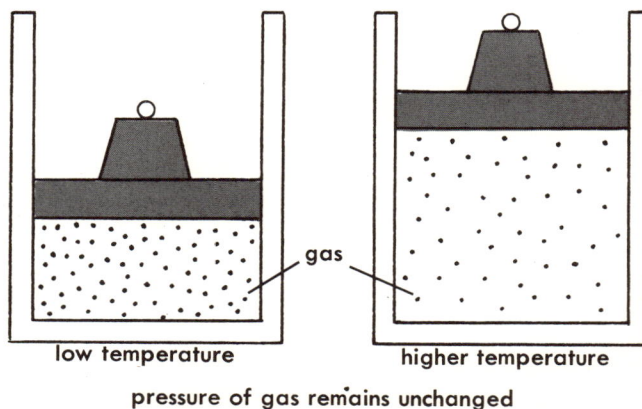

low temperature   higher temperature

pressure of gas remains unchanged

Joseph Louis Gay-Lussac

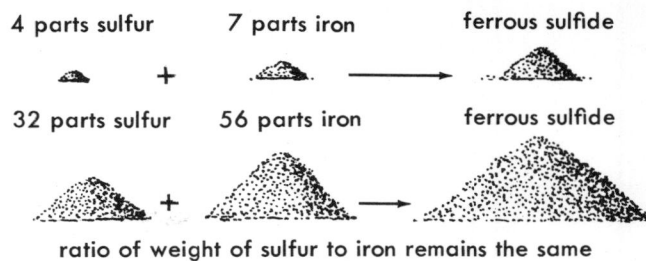

4 parts sulfur   7 parts iron   ferrous sulfide

32 parts sulfur   56 parts iron   ferrous sulfide

ratio of weight of sulfur to iron remains the same

Law of Definite Proportions: All compounds have a definite composition. For example, ferrous sulfide always consists of 56 parts of iron to 32 parts of sulfur; or its ratio by weight is 7 to 4. This law is stated: **In any chemical compound the combination of elements is always in the same proportion by weight.**

Gay-Lussac's Law: During his research on gases, Gay-Lussac discovered that the volume of gases that combine can be expressed by a ratio. For example, two volumes of hydrogen combine with one volume of oxygen and produce two volumes of water vapor (H_2O); or one volume of hydrogen combines with one volume of chlorine to produce two volumes of hydrogen chloride (HCl). Gay-Lussac's law is stated: **The volumes of gases reacting, or resulting from chemical action, can be expressed by a ratio of small whole numbers.**

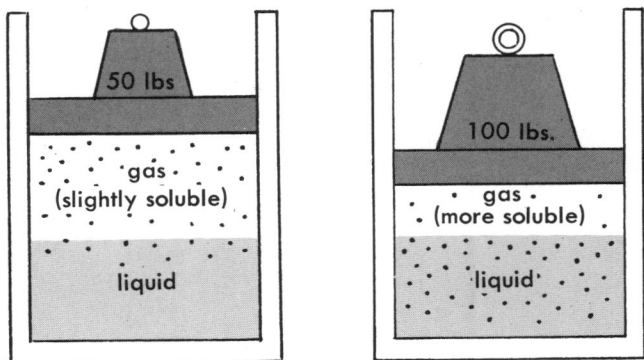

50 lbs

gas
(slightly soluble)

liquid

100 lbs.

gas
(more soluble)

liquid

Henry's Law: The solubility of a gas (carbon dioxide in water, for instance) is increased if the pressure is increased. The carbon dioxide in a bottle of soda water stays in solution because of the high pressure inside the bottle. But when you take off the cap you lower the pressure and the gas comes out of solution. Henry's law describes this action, and is stated: **The solubility of a gas is directly proportional to the pressure which is applied to it.**

John Dalton

Law of Multiple Proportions: Based on his theory that all matter is made up of atoms, John Dalton concluded that when two elements combine and form a variety of compounds, the ratios between the compounds will consist of small whole numbers. For example, water (H_2O) has 7.94 parts of oxygen by weight, whereas hydrogen peroxide (H_2O_2) has 15.88 (2×7.94) parts of oxygen by weight. Then the ratio between the weight of oxygen in water and oxygen in hydrogen peroxide is $1:2$. The law of multiple proportions is stated: **When any two elements, A and B, combine to form more than one compound, the different weights of B, which unite with a fixed weight of A, bear a small whole-number ratio to each other.**

Periodic Law: The properties of elements vary periodically as their atomic numbers. (See *Periodic Table*, pages 68–69.)

The Swedish chemist, Alfred Nobel, amassed a great fortune from his discovery of dynamite and other explosives. Before he died in 1896, he made arrangements for his money to be left in a trust fund, the earnings of which were to be given each year as prizes to people who made outstanding contributions in five fields—physics, chemistry, medicine, literature, and peace.

Each award consists of a gold medal, a diploma, and about $33,000. A prize may be won by one person, or it may be shared by two or more people. Following is a list of the prize winners in chemistry, beginning in the year 1901, when the awards were first made.

YEAR	NAME	NATIONALITY	WORK
1901	Jacobus Hendricus van't Hoff	Dutch	Laws of chemical dynamics and osmotic pressure
1902	Emil Fischer	German	Research on sugar and purine groups
1903	Svante Arrhenius	Swedish	Theory of electrolytic dissociation
1904	Sir William Ramsay	English	Work on inert gases
1905	Adolf von Baeyer	German	Work with dyes and aromatic compounds
1906	Henri Moissan	French	Isolated fluorine; developed the electric furnace
1907	Eduard Buchner	German	Discovered noncellular fermentation
1908	Sir Ernest Rutherford	English	Decay of chemical elements; chemistry of radioactive substances
1909	Wilhelm Ostwald	German	Work on catalysis, chemical equilibrium, rate of chemical reactions
1910	Otto Wallach	German	Work on alicyclic compounds
1911	Marie Curie	French	Discovered radium and polonium
1912	1. Victor Grignard	French	1. Discovered the Grignard reaction
	2. Paul Sabatier	French	2. Hydrogenation of organic compounds
1913	Alfred Werner	Swiss	Research into atoms combined in molecules
1914	Theodore William Richards	U.S.	Determined atomic weights of many substances
1915	Richard Willstätter	German	Research on chlorophyll and other dyestuffs in plants
1916	No award		
1917	No award		
1918	Fritz Haber	German	Synthesized ammonia
1919	No award		
1920	Walter Nernst	German	Work in thermochemistry
1921	Frederick Soddy	English	Research on isotopes
1922	Francis William Aston	English	Research on isotope mixtures
1923	Fritz Pregl	Austrian	Microanalysis of organic materials
1924	No award		
1925	Richard Zsigmondy	German	Work on colloids
1926	Theodor Svedberg	Swedish	Work on dispersion systems
1927	Heinrich Wieland	German	Research on bile acids
1928	Adolf Windaus	German	Sterins and their association with vitamins
1929	1. Sir Arthur Harden	English	1. & 2. Fermentation of sugars
	2. Hans von Euler-Chelpin	Swedish	

YEAR	NAME	NATIONALITY	WORK
1930	Hans Fischer	German	Research on coloring matter of blood and leaves; synthesized hemin
1931	1. Karl Bosch 2. Friedrich Bergius	German German	1. & 2. Development of chemical high-pressure methods
1932	Irving Langmuir	U.S.	Surface chemistry
1933	No award		
1934	Harold Clayton Urey	U.S.	Discovered heavy hydrogen
1935	1. Frédéric Joliot 2. Irène Joliot-Curie	French French	1. & 2. Synthesized new radioactive elements
1936	Peter Debye	German (Dutch-born)	Research on dipole moments and diffraction of X rays and electrons in gases
1937	1. Sir Walter Norman Haworth 2. Paul Karrer	English Swiss	1. Work on carbohydrates and vitamin C 2. Research on vitamins and vegetable dyestuffs
1938	Richard Kuhn	German	Research on vitamins
1939	1. Adolph Butenandt 2. Leopold Ružička	German Swiss (Yugoslav-born)	1. & 2. Work on sexual hormones
1940	No award		
1941	No award		
1942	No award		
1943	Georg von Hevesy	Hungarian	Discoverer (with D. Coster) of hafnium
1944	Otto Hahn	German	Atomic fission
1945	Artturi Virtanen	Finnish	Conservation of fodder
1946	1. James B. Sumner 2. John H. Northrop 3. Wendell M. Stanley	U.S. U.S. U.S.	1. Enzyme crystallization 2. & 3. Prepared enzymes and virus proteins in pure form
1947	Sir Robert Robinson	English	Work on plant products
1948	Arne Tiselius	Swedish	Colloid analysis
1949	William Francis Giauque	U.S.	Effects of low temperatures on matter
1950	1. Otto Diels 2. Kurt Alder	German German	1. & 2. Development of Dien-synthesis
1951	1. Edwin M. McMillan 2. Glenn T. Seaborg	U.S. U.S.	1. & 2. Discovered plutonium
1952	1. Archer J. P. Martin 2. Richard L. M. Synge	English English	1. & 2. Separation of chemical compounds
1953	Hermann Staudinger	German	Work on synthesizing of fiber
1954	Linus C. Pauling	U.S.	Atomic structure of protein molecules
1955	Vincent du Vigneaud	U.S.	Identification and synthesis of hormones
1956	1. Sir Cyril M. Hinshelwood 2. Nikolai Semenov	English Russian	1. & 2. Mechanism of chemical reactions
1957	Sir Alexander Todd	English	Chemical composition of cell nucleus
1958	Frederick Sanger	English	Research on the structure of the protein hormone insulin
1959	Jaroslav Heyrovsky	Czechoslovak	Polarography
1960	Willard F. Libby	U.S.	Discoverer of radiocarbon dating
1961	Melvin Calvin	U.S.	The role of carbon in photosynthesis
1962	1. John C. Kendrew 2. Max F. Perutz	English Austrian	1. & 2. Discoverers of the structure of two of the most important of the globular protein molecules—hemoglobin and myoglobin

A SELECTION OF COMMON ALLOYS

NAME	PER CENT COMPOSITION	USES
Acid-resisting iron	Fe 86; Cr 13	
Alkali-resisting iron	Fe 95; Ni 5	
Aluminum brass	Cu 71–75; Zn 26–42; Al 1–6	Propeller blades and marine fittings
Aluminum bronze	Cu 89–99; Al 1–11	
Aver metal	Fe 35; Ce 35; La 24; Yb 3	Sparking metal used in cigarette and gas lighters
Babbitt metal	Sn 89; Sb 7.3; Cu 3.7	Bearings
Battery plate	Pb 94; Sb 6	Storage batteries
Bearing metal	Pb 98; Ba 2	Antifriction bearings
Bell metal	Cu 75–80; Sn 20–25	Bells
Brass	Cu 60–90; Zn 10–40	Pipes, hardware
Britannia metal	Zn 85–90; Sb 5–10; Cu 1–3	Antique tableware
Bronze	Cu 81; Sn 19	Statues, ornamental work, hardware
Carboloy	Tungsten carbide and cobalt	Grinding tools
Constantan	Cu 45–60; Ni 40–55; Mn 1–1.4; small amounts of C and Fe	Thermocouples
Delta metal	Cu 54–56; Zn 40–44; Fe 0.9–1.3; Mn 0.8–1.4; Pb 0.4–1.8	Marine fittings
Dow metal	Mg 90–96; Al 4–10; some Mn	Aircraft parts, typewriters, cameras
Duraluminum	Al 95; Cu 4; Mn 0.5; Mg 0.5	Aircraft parts
Duriron	Fe; Si 14–15; Mn 2–2.5; C 0.8–1.3; S 0.05–0.2; P 0.05–1	Used where acids may attack the metal
German silver	Cu 55; Zn 25; Ni 20	Substitute for silver
Green gold	Au 75; Ag 11–25; Cd 0–13	Jewelry
Gun metal	Cu 71–95; Sn 0–11; Pb 0–13; Zn 0–5; Fe 0–1.4	Gears, badges, trays
Magnalium	Al 70–95; Mg 5–30	Scientific instruments
Monel metal	Ni 68; Cu 28; Fe 1.9	Sinks
Nichrome	Ni 54–80; Cr 10–22; Fe 4.8–27	Wire for electric heating units

This sketch, based on Egyptian records dating about 1500 B.C., shows bronze being cast. At left, men melt the metals in a furnace with foot bellows. At center, they remove the crucible from the flames, then pour the molten metal into molds on the casting table.

A SELECTION OF COMMON ALLOYS

NAME	PER CENT COMPOSITION	USES
Nickel coin	Cu 75; Ni 25	Coin
One-cent piece	Cu 95; Sn 3; Zn 2	Coin
Palau	Au 80; Pd 20	A substitute for platinum
Permalloy	Ni 78; Fe 21; Co 0.4; Mn; Cu; C; S; Si	Telephone cables
Pewter	Sn 74–89; Pb 0–20; Sb 0–7.6; Cu 0–3.5; Zn	Antique plates, drinking cups
Shot metal	Pb 99; As 1	Shot and bullets
Silver—coins	Ag 90; Cu 10	Coins
Silver—sterling	Ag 80; Zn 18; Cu 2.5	Silverware
Solder (soft)	Pb 50; Sn 50	Joining metals
Steel	Mostly Fe with small amounts of:	
Carbon (high)	C 0.75–1.4	Tools and springs
Carbon (medium)	C 0.25–0.75	Axles, rails, wheels
Carbon (low)	C 0.05–0.25	Bridge girders, cars, ships, buildings, nails
Chrome	Cr 3	Files, ball bearings, safes
Chromium-tungsten	C 0.25–1; W 5–25; Cr 2–10; V 0.25–1	High-speed tools
Chromium-vanadium	C 0.25–1; Cr 0.8–1.1; V 0.15; Mn 6–15	Gears and axles, steam shovels
Molybdenum	Mo 0.3–3	Axles
Nickel	Ni 3–4	Bridges, cables, crankshafts
Nickel-chromium	Ni 1–4; Cr 0.45–2	Armor plate
Stellite	Co 55–80; Cr 20–35; W 0–10	Surgical instruments
Tinfoil	Sn 88; Pb 8; Cu 4; Sb 0.5	Wrappings for food (now largely replaced by plastics)
Type metal	Pb 56–60; Sn 10–40; Sb 4.5–30	Printing type
Wood's metal	Bi 50; Pb 25; Sn 12.5; Cd 12.5	Low-melting: used as plugs in automatic fire sprinklers

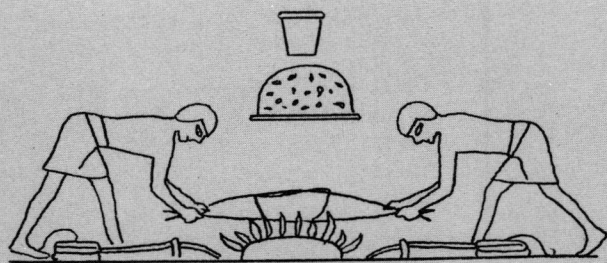

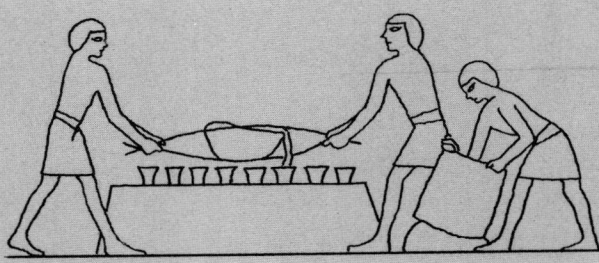

Today's synthetic fibers are in many respects superior to natural fibers. What makes them superior is their greater tensile strength, resistance to moths and mildew, wrinkling and abrasion, and their resistance to the action of water and household chemicals which frequently damage natural fibers.

The chemist's first step in producing synthetic fibers—whether the fiber is rayon, nylon, orlon, or others—is to prepare a fluid batch of the material. Once this is done he forces the fluid under pressure through a small nozzlelike disk, called a "spinneret," which may have more than 100 tiny holes. The size of the holes determines the size of the synthetic thread.

As fluid threads stream out of the holes of the spinneret, they are coagulated either in a liquid acid bath or in a current of air. If a bath is used, the process is called "wet-spinning"; if air is used, "dry-spinning."

Rayon: Regenerated cellulose. Nearly all of the synthetic rayon we use is **viscose** rayon. It is made from sheets of cellulose pulp which is soaked in a lye solution and treated with carbon disulfide. After being dissolved in more lye solution, the product called viscose is obtained. It is this material that is forced through a spinneret and comes out of the wet-spinning process as rayon thread or ribbon.

Nylon: Synthesized from air, water, and coal or petroleum by condensation polymerization (see **Polymerization**). At the proper stage of condensation the liquid is evaporated, then the residue is heated under pressure. The resulting liquid nylon is next forced through a spinneret to produce threads, or it is made into ribbon, sheets, or solid objects. The threads are stretched to about four times their original length, producing elastic, transparent strands. Nylon, which resembles silk, is superior to silk in many ways: it is stronger, longer wearing, and more resistant to the action of water and household chemicals. In addition to its use as a fabric, nylon is used as brush bristles, rope, and insulation-coating for metal wire.

Protein Fibers: Protein, like cellulose, can be treated (regenerated) to produce fibers resembling wool. From milk casein comes the fiber **Aralac;** from corn zein, **Vicara;** from peanut protein, **Saralon.** Because these protein fibers are usually weakened by the action of water, they are strengthened by a blend of natural wool or some other fiber. **Dacron** and **Lanital** are also synthetic protein fibers.

Dinyl: The trade name of a fiber made from vinyl chloride and acrylonitrile. It resists moths, fungi, mildew, fire, and mild acids.

Orlon: An acrylic fiber with strong weather-resisting properties. It is used in sailmaking and tentmaking, for drapes and summer suits.

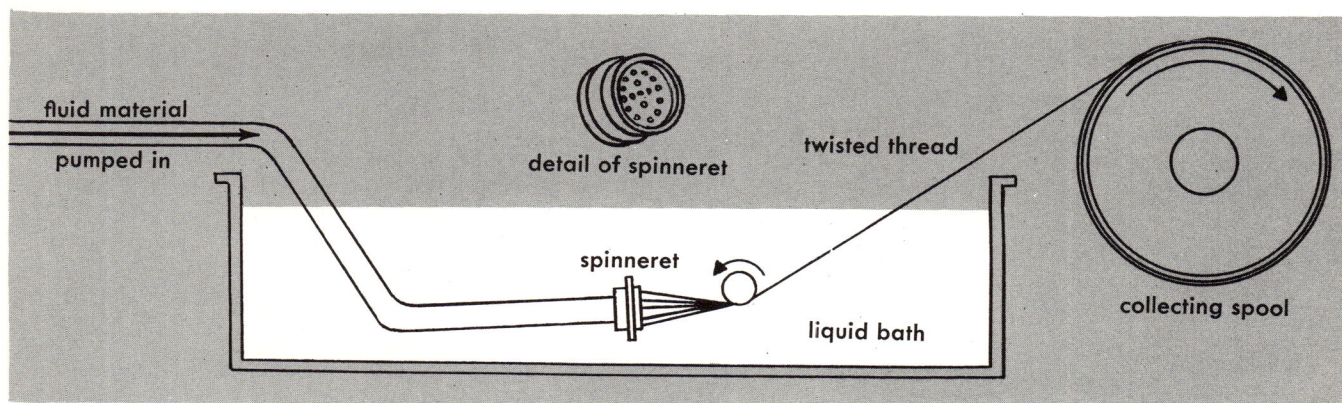

Diagram shows the wet-spinning process for making synthetic fibers. As the fluid threads stream out of the spinneret they are coagulated in a liquid bath and then wound onto a collecting spool.

SOME COMMON SYNTHETIC RUBBERS

NAME	CHARACTERISTICS	USES	COMPARED WITH NATURAL RUBBER
Buna S (GR-S^2)	Easily vulcanized; becomes hot at high speeds or under heavy pressure	Tires; can be mixed with natural rubber	Resists weathering and abrasion well, but does not resist oil and chemicals particularly well
Butyl (GR-l)	Good all-around rubber	Excellent for use in inner tubes, since it holds air better than natural rubber; resists aging well	Resists weathering, chemicals, ozone well, but resists abrasion only fairly well
Neoprene (GR-M)	Neither sulfur nor carbon is needed for vulcanization	Many military uses, for example, self-sealing fuel tanks	Highly resistant to weathering, abrasion, oil, and chemicals
Buna N (Perbunan)	A special-purpose rubber because its characteristics vary, depending on the proportion of butadiene and acrylonitrile of which it is made	Gaskets; self-sealing fuel tanks; covering for cables; airplane parts	Resistant to heat, but not as resistant to light as natural rubber; resists oil, abrasion, and chemicals well
Thiokol	Resists oils and fats well, but has an unpleasant odor	Recapping tires	Resists weathering well, but is weakened by heat and abrasion; highly resistant to oil and chemicals
Koroseal	Cannot be vulcanized; is not particularly tough	Used for waterproofing and in making chemical equipment	Although softened by heat, it resists weathering very well; also resists abrasion, oil, and chemicals very well

COURTESY UNITED STATES RUBBER

Molding a tire: Synthetic rubber, in the shape of a barrel, is placed over an inflatable "shaping bag" (left) before vulcanizing and molding. Finished tire, complete with treads, is removed from mold (right).

THE METRIC SYSTEM

1 meter	=	10	decimeters (dm.)
1 dm.	=	10	centimeters (cm.)
1 cm.	=	10	millimeters (mm.)
1 mm.	=	1000	microns (μ)
1000 m.	=	1	kilometer (km.)
1 liter	=	1000	milliliters (ml.)
1 liter	=	1	cu. dm.
1 kilogram (kg.)	=	1000	grams (g.)
1 g.	=	1000	milligrams (mg.)

CONVERSION FACTORS

1 meter	=	39.37	inches
1 inch	=	2.54	centimeters
1 quart (liquid)	=	.946	liters
1 liter	=	1.057	quarts (liquid)
1 kilogram	=	2.205	pounds
1 pound	=	453.6	grams
1 ounce (fluid)	=	29.57	milliliters
1 ounce (avoir.)	=	28.35	grams
1 gram	=	15.432	grains
1 ton (short)	=	907.185	kilograms
1 cubic yard	=	.765	cubic meters
1 cubic inch	=	16.387	milliliters

ELEMENTS CONTAINED IN THE HUMAN BODY

ELEMENT		PER CENT
C	Carbon	18.
N	Nitrogen	3.
Ca	Calcium	1.5
P	Phosphorus	1.
K	Potassium	0.35
S	Sulfur	0.25
Na	Sodium	0.15
Cl	Chlorine	0.15
Mg	Magnesium	0.03
Fe	Iron	0.01
Si	Silicon	0.01
Zn	Zinc	0.003
F	Fluorine	0.002
Cu	Copper	0.0002
Mn	Manganese	0.0001
I	Iodine	0.0001
As	Arsenic	0.00001
Co	Cobalt	0.000001

ELEMENTS COMPOSING THE EARTH

ELEMENT	PERCENTAGE BY WEIGHT
Iron	39.76
Oxygen	27.71
Silicon	14.53
Magnesium	8.69
Nickel	3.16
Calcium	2.52
Aluminum	1.79
Sulfur	0.64
Sodium	0.39
Cobalt	0.23
Chromium	0.20
Potassium	0.14
Phosphorus	0.11
Manganese	0.07
Carbon	0.04
Titanium	0.02

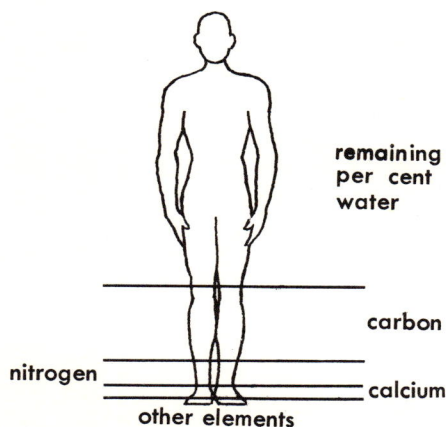

remaining per cent water

carbon

nitrogen

calcium

other elements

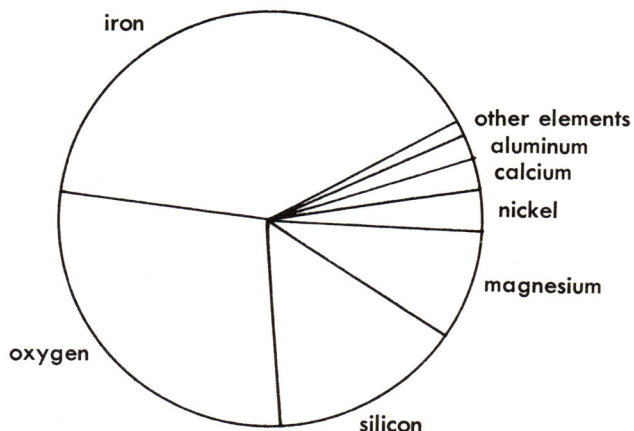

iron

other elements
aluminum
calcium

nickel

magnesium

oxygen

silicon

VITAMINS—THEIR SOURCES AND FUNCTIONS
(not a complete list)

NAME	FORMULA	PRESENT IN	DEFICIENCY CAUSES
Vitamin A (Hemi-carotene)	$C_{20}H_{29}O$	Egg yolk, milk, butter, fish-liver oils, carrots, tomatoes	Night blindness or more serious eye trouble; respiratory diseases, and loss of weight
Vitamin B₁ (Thiamin) (Aneurin)	$C_{12}H_{17}N_4OSCl \cdot HCl$	Green vegetables, wheat germ, yeast, egg yolk	Beriberi, nervous disorders
Vitamin B₂ (G) (Riboflavin) (Lactoflavin)	$C_{17}H_{20}N_4O_6$	Liver, yeast, muscle, green vegetables, milk, egg yolk, wheat germ	Slow growth in children, loss of hair, skin abnormalities, eye disease
Vitamin B₄ or B₅ (Niacin) (Nicotinic acid)	$C_6H_5NO_2$	Liver, yeast, peanuts, eggs, fish, leafy vegetables, milk	Pellagra (skin disturbances, nervous disorders, digestion disorders)
Vitamin B₆ (Pyridoxine)	$C_8H_{11}NO_3 \cdot HCl$	Yeast, liver, rice, bran, maize	Slow growth, muscular disorders
Vitamin B₁₂ (Cyanocobalamin)	$C_{61-64}H_{86-92}N_{14}O_{13}PCo$	Liver	Pernicious anemia
Vitamin C (Ascorbic acid)	$C_6H_8O_6$	Citrus fruits, tomatoes, uncooked, fresh, leafy vegetables, potatoes	Scurvy
Vitamin D (Calciferol)	$C_{28}H_{44}O$	Liver oils, milk, butter. Formed in the skin by the action of sunlight	Rickets
Vitamin E (Tocophorol)	$C_{29}H_{50}O_2$	Green vegetables, wheat germ, meat, egg yolks	Sterility in rats
Vitamin K K₁ K₂	$C_{31}H_{46}O_2$ $C_{41}H_{56}O_2$	Tomatoes, alfalfa, egg yolk, liver, leafy vegetables	Hemorrhages

VITAMIN A carrots, butter, egg yolk

VITAMIN B₁ green vegetables wheat germ

VITAMIN B₄, B₅ liver, fish, peanuts

VITAMIN C leafy vegetables citrus fruits

VITAMIN D butter, milk, sunlight

AVERAGE COMPOSITION OF EDIBLE PORTION OF TYPICAL FOODS
EXPRESSED IN GRAMS PER 100 GRAMS OF FOOD

FOOD	WATER	PROTEIN	FAT	CARBO-HYDRATE	FUEL VALUE (Cal. per 100 g.)
Apples	84.6	0.4	0.5	14.2	63
Asparagus	94.0	1.8	0.2	3.3	22
Bacon (smoked)	20.2	9.9	64.8		623
Bananas	75.3	1.3	0.6	22.0	99
Beans (dried)	12.6	2.5	1.8	59.6	345
Beans (string)	89.2	2.3	0.3	7.4	42
Beef (lean steak)	70.0	21.0	2.9		115
Beef (slightly fat)	73.8	22.1	7.9		155
Beets	87.5	1.6	0.1	9.7	46
Bread (corn)	38.9	7.9	4.7	46.3	259
Bread (graham)	35.7	8.9	1.8	52.1	260
Bread (white)	35.3	9.2	1.3	53.1	260
Butter	11.0	1.0	85.0		769
Cabbage	91.5	1.6	0.3	5.6	32
Carrots	88.2	1.1	0.4	9.3	45
Celery	94.5	1.1	0.1	3.3	19
Chicken	63.7	19.3	16.3		224
Codfish (fresh)	82.6	15.8	0.4		67
Corn (green)	75.4	3.1	1.1	19.7	101
Eggs	73.7	14.8	10.5		154
Ham (lean, smoked)	53.5	20.2	20.8		268
Lettuce	94.7	1.2	0.3	2.0	16
Milk	87.0	3.3	4.0	5.0	69
Oatmeal	7.3	6.1	7.2	67.5	400
Oranges	86.9	0.8	0.2	11.6	51
Peaches	89.4	0.7	0.1	9.4	41
Peanuts	9.2	25.8	38.6	24.4	548
Peas (green)	74.6	7.0	0.5	16.9	100
Potatoes	78.3	2.2	0.1	18.4	83
Prunes (dried)	22.3	2.1		73.3	302
Rice	12.3	8.0	0.3	79.0	351
Salmon	64.6	21.2	12.8		200
Spinach	92.3	2.1	0.3	3.2	24
Tomatoes	94.3	0.9	0.4	3.9	23
Turnips	89.6	1.3	0.2	8.1	40

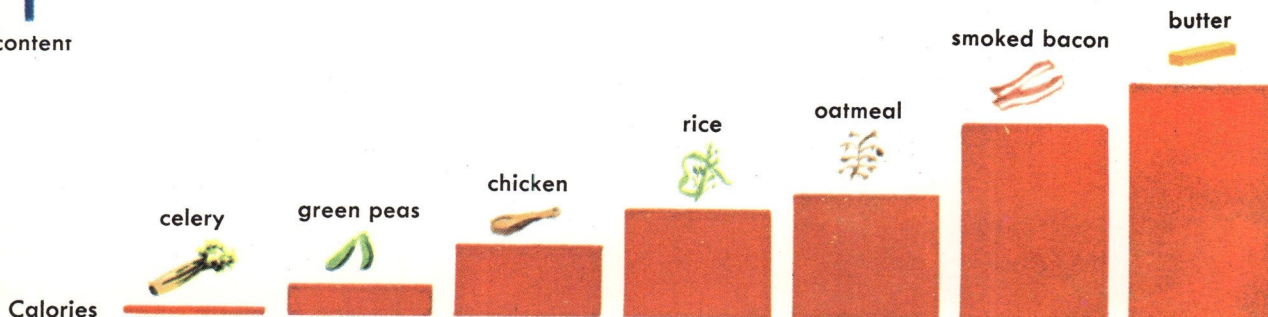

rice

oatmeal

peanuts

potatoes

lettuce

carbohydrate content

celery

green peas

chicken

rice

oatmeal

smoked bacon

butter

Calories

WHAT ARE ACIDS?

Acids are electrolytes which in solution give up hydrogen ions (protons). The number of hydrogen ions which a given amount of acid can give up (called the degree of ionization) determines just how strong the acid is. In general, acids have these things in common:

1. They affect indicators, meaning that they turn litmus paper red.
2. They have a sour taste, as is found in vinegar and lemons.

3. They react with:
   a. carbonates—producing carbon dioxide, CO_2
   b. sulfites—producing sulfur dioxide, SO_2
   c. sulfides—producing hydrogen sulfide, H_2S
   d. bases—producing salt and water
   e. metal oxides—producing salt and water
   f. active metals—producing salt and hydrogen

There are many different kinds of acids. Some occur in nature, others are made only by man. Some common laboratory acids are listed here:

NAME	COMMON NAME	FORMULA	USED IN
Acetic acid	(dilute as vinegar)	$HC_2H_3O_2$	Making acetates, cellulose acetate
Hydrochloric acid	Muriatic acid	HCl	Cleaning metal surfaces (found in the stomach)
Nitric acid		HNO_3	Making fertilizers, explosives, dyes
Orthophosphoric	Phosphoric acid	H_3PO_4	Making phosphates
Sulfuric acid	Oil of vitriol	H_2SO_4	Car batteries, and making chemicals

The sour taste of many fruits and vegetables is due to the presence of organic acids. Listed here are some common foods and the organic acids they contain:

ACID	FORMULA	FOUND IN
Benzoic	$HC_7H_5O_2$	Cranberries
Citric	$H_3C_6H_5O_7$	Citrus fruits
Lactic	$HC_3H_5O_3$	Sour milk, sauerkraut
Malic	$H_2C_4H_4O_5$	Green apples
Oxalic	$HC_2H_2O_4$	Rhubarb, sorrel
Salicylic	$HC_7H_5O_3$	Wintergreen
Tartaric	$H_2C_4H_4O_6$	Grapes

Many other acids such as acetyl salicylic acid (aspirin), barbituric, pyruvic, hippuric are important to man. Some of these are used either as medicinals or their products are used. Other acids are found in the body and are useful in maintaining good health. Amino acids, for instance, are the basic building blocks from which protein tissues are built. Stored foods such as fats are organic salts (esters) of fatty acids and glycerol. Some of the vitamins are acids; these include: nicotinic acid, folic acid, and ascorbic acid.

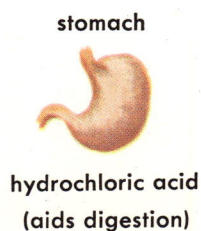

battery

sulfuric acid
(electrolyte solution)

stomach

hydrochloric acid
(aids digestion)

sprinkler

nitric acid
(fertilizer)

lemons

citric acid
(present in fruits)

milk

lactic acid
(sour milk)

SOME COMMON PLASTICS I (Thermosetting)

NAME	CHARACTERISTICS	USES
Cast Phenolics Bakelite, Catalin, Prystal, Durite	A variety of colors; not so durable as molded phenolics; sunlight may cause light colors to fade	Clock and radio cases; table and kitchen items, trays
Melamines Melamine, Duralite, Plaskon, Hemcoware, Resimene, Panelyte	All colors; sunlight or heat may cause darkening; translucent or opaque; durable and extremely hard; odorless; do not give food a foreign taste	Containers for food; tableware; lighting fixtures; refrigerator coatings; radio casings
Molded Phenolics Bakelite, Durez, Resinox	A variety of colors; inexpensive, durable; nonconductors of electricity	Electric plugs; clock and radio cases; telephones, insulators, vacuum cleaners
Polyesters Plaskon, Laminac, Vibrin, Kriston, Glyptal	All colors; very strong; do not lend themselves well to molding; "scuff proof"	Coatings and laminates; clock cases and desk sets
Ureas Plaston, Beetle, Hemcoware	A variety of colors; translucent or opaque; sunlight or heat may cause light colors to fade; fairly strong; odorless; do not give food a foreign taste	Novelty objects; radio and clock cases; games

1 THERMOSETTING PLASTICS: The plastics that belong to this group can be made from the basic ingredients coal, air, and water. The resin (see diagram on this page below) is shaped as an end product when heat and pressure are applied. The thermosetting plastics remain hard. They do not soften when they are reheated.

2 THERMOPLASTIC PLASTICS: The plastics that belong to this group can be made from the basic ingredients coal and natural gas. Once formed into an end product, the resin (see diagram on page 85) can be reheated, softened, and reshaped again and again. This is the major difference between thermoplastic and thermosetting plastics.

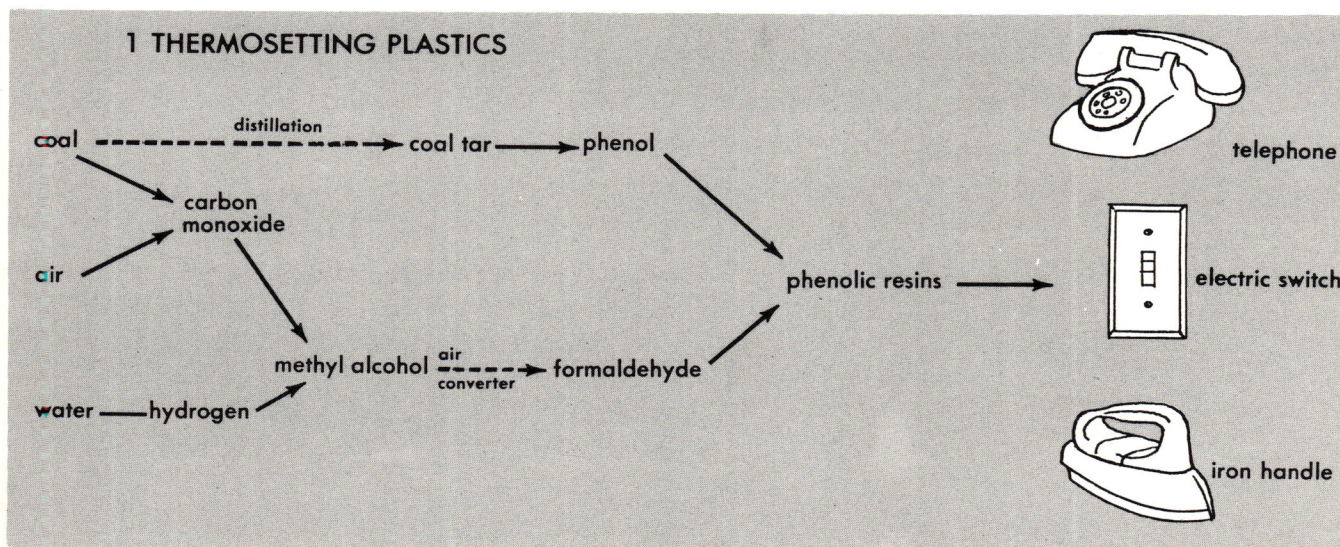

1 THERMOSETTING PLASTICS

coal ---- distillation ----> coal tar ----> phenol
coal ----> carbon monoxide
air ----> carbon monoxide
carbon monoxide ----> methyl alcohol
water ---- hydrogen ----> methyl alcohol
methyl alcohol --air converter--> formaldehyde
phenol ----> phenolic resins
formaldehyde ----> phenolic resins
phenolic resins ---->

telephone

electric switch

iron handle

SOME COMMON PLASTICS II (Thermoplastics)

NAME	CHARACTERISTICS	USES
Acrylics Lucite, Plexiglas, Acryloid, Crystalite	Glasslike; conducts light; does not give food a foreign taste; odorless; scratches easily but polishes well	Lamp and brush bases; combs and frames; aircraft windows and lenses; directional signs
Cellulose Celluloid, Celcon, Plastacele, Tenite, Pyralin, Lumarith, Ethocel, Cellophane, Methocel, Fortecel	Strong and light in weight; most are odorless and do not give food a foreign taste, but some do; those cellulose plastics containing nitrate should be kept away from flame	Toys; combs; pens; table mats; flashlight cases; wrappings; lamp shades; bowls
Nylon	Elastic and strong; does not tear, wrinkle, or break easily; resists the action of water and household chemicals	Stockings and suits; combs and brush bristles
Polystyrene Styron, Lustrex, Bakelite, Lustron, Loalin, Plexene, Miraplas	Although light in weight, it may be brittle; sunlight may turn it yellow; resistant to many chemicals; odorless and does not give food a foreign taste	Wall tiles and toilet articles; jewelry; food containers; radio cases and kitchen accessories; stoppers for containers of corrosive materials
Vinyl (1) Vinylite, Duprene, Vinyon, Koroseal, Geon, Marvalon, Alluron, Krene	Strong and resistant to mildew and fungus; transparent, translucent, or opaque; waterproof, but not particularly resistant to chemicals	Garment bags and shower curtains; tiles and handles; table covers and mats; draperies, wallpaper and upholstery; insulation
Vinyl (2) Lumite, Saran, Velon	Similar to the Vinyl (1) materials, but resistant to chemicals	Similar to the Vinyl (1) materials' uses, but wider uses because of resistance to chemicals

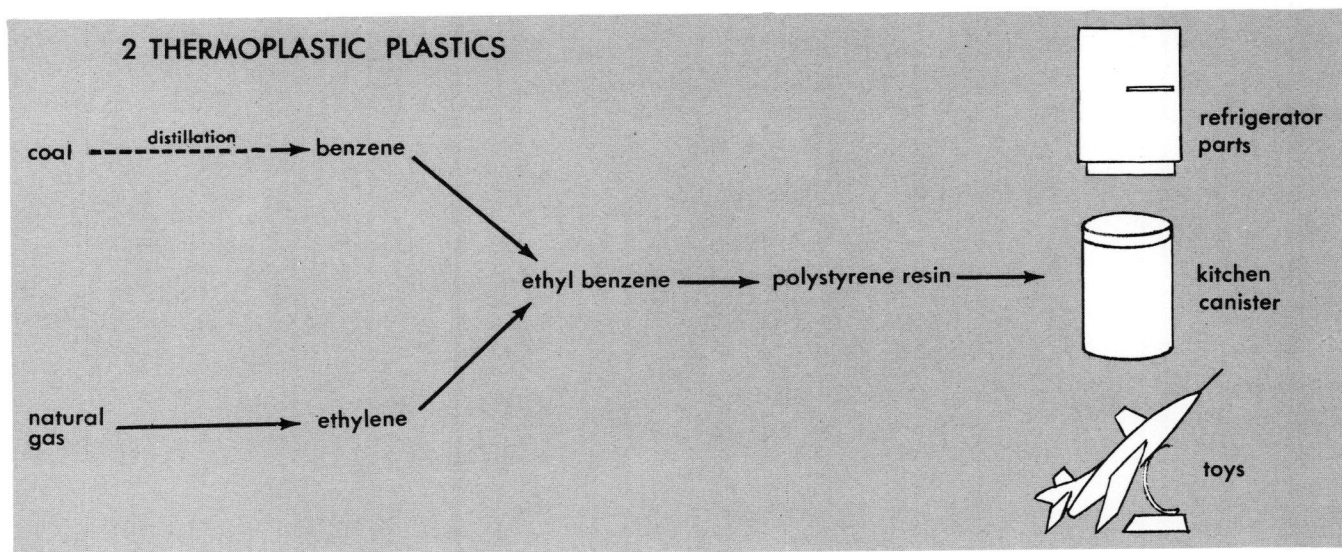

2 THERMOPLASTIC PLASTICS

coal - - - distillation - - -> benzene

natural gas ———> ethylene

benzene + ethylene —> ethyl benzene ——> polystyrene resin ——>

refrigerator parts

kitchen canister

toys

COMMON SUBSTANCES AND THEIR CHEMICAL NAMES

COMMON NAME	CHEMICAL NAME	FORMULA
Alum	Potassium aluminum sulfate	$K_2SO_4 \cdot Al_2(SO_4)_3 \cdot 24H_2O$
Ammonia water	Ammonium hydroxide	NH_4OH
Asbestos	Magnesium silicate	$Mg_3Si_2O_7 \cdot 2H_2O$
Baking soda	Sodium hydrogen carbonate	$NaHCO_3$
Bauxite	Aluminum oxide	$Al_2O_3 \cdot 2H_2O$
Bicarbonate of soda	Sodium bicarbonate	$NaHCO_3$
Bleaching powder	Calcium hypochlorite	$Ca(ClO)_2$
Blue vitriol	Copper sulfate, crystals	$CuSO_4 \cdot 5H_2O$
Borax	Sodium tetraborate	$Na_2B_4O_7 \cdot 10H_2O$
Calcite	Calcium carbonate	$CaCO_3$
Calomel	Mercurous chloride	$HgCl$
Caustic potash	Potassium hydroxide	KOH
Caustic soda	Sodium hydroxide	$NaOH$
Chile saltpeter	Sodium nitrate	$NaNO_3^+$
Cinnabar	Mercuric sulfide	HgS
Clorox	Sodium hypochlorite solution	$NaClO$
Corrosive sublimate	Mercuric chloride	$HgCl_2$
Cream of tartar	Potassium hydrogen tartrate	$KHC_4H_4O_6$
Cryolite	Sodium aluminum fluoride	Na_3AlF_6
Epsom salt	Magnesium sulfate, crystals	$MgSO_4 \cdot 7H_2O$
Fire damp	Methane (mixed with air)	$CH_4 + air$
Flowers of sulfur	Sulfur, powdered	S
Gypsum	Calcium sulfate	$CaSO_4 \cdot 2H_2O$
Household ammonia	Ammonium hydroxide	NH_4OH
Hypo	Sodium thiosulfate	$Na_2S_2O_3 \cdot 5H_2O$
Laughing gas	Nitrous oxide	N_2O
Lime, quick	Calcium oxide	CaO
Limestone	Calcium carbonate	$CaCO_3$
Limewater	Calcium hydroxide solution	$Ca(OH)_2$
Lunar caustic	Silver nitrate	$AgNO_3$
Magnesia	Magnesium oxide	MgO
Marsh gas	Methane	CH_4
Moth balls	Naphthalene	$C_{10}H_8$
Peroxide	Hydrogen peroxide	H_2O_2
Plaster of Paris	Calcium sulfate	$(CaSO_4)_2 \cdot H_2O$
Potash	Potassium carbonate	K_2CO_3
Quartz	Silicon dioxide	SiO_2
Quicklime	Calcium oxide	CaO
Rochelle salt	Sodium potassium tartrate	$NaKC_4H_4O_6$
Sal ammoniac	Ammonium chloride	NH_4Cl
Sal soda	Sodium carbonate	$Na_2CO_3 \cdot 10H_2O$
Salt, table	Sodium chloride	$NaCl$

COMMON SUBSTANCES (continued)

COMMON NAME	CHEMICAL NAME	FORMULA
Saltpeter	Potassium nitrate	KNO_3
Slaked lime	Calcium hydroxide	$Ca(OH)_2$
Soda ash	Sodium carbonate	Na_2CO_3
Soap	Sodium stearate (mainly)	$C_{17}H_{35}COONa$
Sugar	Sucrose	$C_{12}H_{22}O_{11}$
Vinegar	Acetic acid, (weak)	$HC_2H_3O_2$
Washing soda	Sodium carbonate	$Na_2CO_3 \cdot 10H_2O$
Water glass	Sodium silicate	Na_2SiO_3

COURTESY LESLIE SALT COMPANY

Common salt (NaCl) can be produced by evaporating sea water. This 200,000-ton pile is the result of solar evaporation. For another source of salt, see page 59.

ELEMENTS COMPOSING THE EARTH'S CRUST (atmosphere, sea, and crust)

ELEMENT	PERCENTAGE BY WEIGHT
Oxygen	49.5
Silicon	25.7
Aluminum	7.5
Iron	4.7
Calcium	3.4
Sodium	2.6
Potassium	2.4
Magnesium	1.9
Hydrogen	0.87
Titanium	0.58
All others	0.85

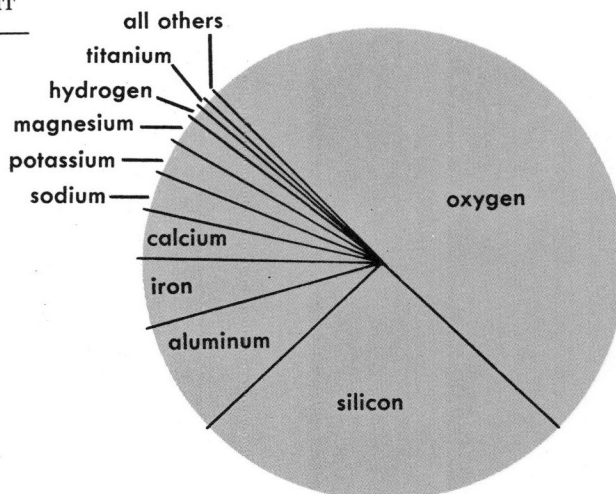

SOLUBILITY TABLE

When you are doing laboratory work you often need to know if a substance is soluble. The table on this page will tell you. For example, read down the column headed "Chloride." You will find that a chloride of aluminum is soluble, but that chlorides of mercurous mercury and silver are insoluble. On reading across the table along the entry "copper" you will see that a carbonate, hydroxide, oxide and so on of copper are insoluble.

Solubility Rules

In addition to the table, the following solubility rules should be helpful:

1. All acetates, chlorates, and nitrates are soluble.

2. All common compounds of ammonium, potassium, and sodium are soluble.

3. All chlorides, bromides, and iodides are soluble except those of silver, mercurous mercury, and lead.

4. All sulfates are soluble except those of barium, lead, and strontium.

5. All bicarbonates are soluble.

6. All common carbonates, silicates, phosphates, and sulfides are insoluble—except those of sodium, potassium, and ammonium.

7. All common hydroxides are insoluble except those of sodium, potassium, and ammonium. Barium and calcium hydroxides are slightly soluble.

s soluble in water
sl slightly soluble in water

sa insoluble in water, soluble in acids
ia insoluble in water, insoluble in acids

	Acetate	Bromide	Carbonate	Chlorate	Chloride	Chromate	Hydroxide	Iodide	Nitrate	Oxide	Phosphate	Sulfate	Sulfide	Sulfite
Aluminum	s	s	–	s	s	–	sa	s	s	sa	sa	s	–	–
Ammonium	s	s	s	s	s	s	s	s	s	–	s	s	s	s
Barium	s	s	sa	s	s	sa	s	s	s	s	sa	ia	–	sa
Calcium	s	s	sa	s	s	sa	sl	s	s	sl	sa	sl	–	sa
Copper (ic)	s	s	sa	s	s	sa	sa	s	s	sa	sa	s	ia	–
Iron (ous)	s	s	sa	–	s	–	sa	s	s	sa	sa	s	sa	sa
Iron (ic)	sa	s	–	–	s	–	sa	s	s	sa	sa	s	–	–
Lead	s	sl	sa	s	sl	sa	sa	sl	s	sa	sa	ia	ia	sa
Magnesium	s	s	sa	s	s	s	sa	s	s	sa	sa	s	–	sl
Manganese (ous)	s	s	sa	–	s	–	sa	s	s	sa	sa	s	sa	–
Mercury (ous)	sa	ia	sa	s	ia	sl	–	ia	s	–	–	sa	ia	–
Mercury (ic)	s	s	sa	s	s	sl	–	sl	s	sa	sa	sa	ia	–
Potassium	s	s	s	s	s	s	s	s	s	s	s	s	s	s
Silver	sl	ia	sa	s	ia	sa	–	ia	s	sa	sa	sa	ia	sa
Sodium	s	s	s	s	s	s	s	s	s	s	s	s	s	s
Strontium	s	s	sa	s	s	sa	sl	s	s	sl	sa	ia	–	sa
Zinc	s	s	sa	s	s	sa	sa	s	s	sa	sa	s	sa	sa